Volume 2, Number 4   *Winter, 1981*

INFANT MENTAL HEALTH JOURNAL

JOURNAL REVIEWS

The INFANT MENTAL HEALTH JOURNAL is the official publication of the Michigan Association for Mental Health. The JOURNAL is dedicated to an interdisciplinary approach to the optimal development of infants, and will bring together ideas, programs and approaches from many different caregiving specialties. Articles will include original research and practical programs as well as review articles.

Purposes, policies, bylaws and formal actions of the MICHIGAN ASSOCIATION FOR INFANT MENTAL HEALTH will be included in a section in the JOURNAL. Upon the creation of other state associations and national or international associations for infant mental health, announcements of their official actions will be included in this section. Members of affiliated associations are eligible for subscriptions at reduced rates.

MANUSCRIPTS should be submitted to the Editor in triplicate (original and two copies), typed on one side of the page only, with double spacing throughout. Style should conform to that found in these pages. References should be numbered in the text in order of citation and should be listed following the style used by *Index Medicus*. Additional questions regarding style and submission of manuscripts should be directed to the Editor, Jack M. Stack, MD, 510 Prospect, Alma, MI 48801.

ABSTRACTED in *Psychological Abstracts.*

INDEXED in *Current Journal Literature, Social Science Documentation Center.*

SUBSCRIPTIONS are on a calendar year basis: $23.00 per year. Institutional rates are $48.00; information regarding student rates may be obtained from the business office. Prices are slightly higher outside the U.S. ADVERTISING and subscription inquiries should be made to Human Sciences Press, 72 Fifth Ave., New York, NY 10011 (212) 243-6000.

ISSN 0163-9641   IMHJDZ2(4)209-296(1981)

Fathers and Infants

A Special Issue of
Infant Mental Health Journal

Hiram E. Fitzgerald, PhD
Cathleen Erin McGreal, MA
Guest Editors

HUMAN SCIENCES PRESS, INC.
72 Fifth Avenue • 3 Henrietta Street
NEW YORK, NY 10011 • LONDON, WC2E 8LU

Library of Congress Catalog Number 81-82739
ISBN: 0-89885-121-1
Copyright 1981 by Human Sciences Press

HUMAN SCIENCES PRESS
72 Fifth Avenue
New York, NY 10011

Printed in the United States of America

Infant Mental Health Journal, Vol. 2, No. 4, Winter 1981

Editor's Note

Fathers and Infants

We are indebted to our guest editors and the authors of the papers on infants and fathers for helping us focus on this very special topic. Although over the past decade we have seen an upsurge in research interest in fathers, it may be helpful to us to remember that this new interest does not necessarily reflect that fathers' interest in their own infants is new. Consider the intense interest in their own infants demonstrated by Charles Darwin and Jean Piaget. Current research is confirming that fathers are both caring and competent. Whenever as scientists we think we have learned something new, it is always a humbling experience to find that the artist or poet knew it long before we did. Standing in the Louvre in Paris is the statue (opposite) which is a replica of a 4th century B. C. sculpure. Clearly this ancient sculptor captured for us the very essence of a caring and competent father.

Jack M. Stack, MD
Editor

Introduction

This special issue of the *Infant Mental Health Journal* is dedicated to fathers and their infants. Twenty years ago few professionals gave serious thought to mental health for infants and their families. Infant care was viewed in the context of physical health and basic caregiving, and these were responsibilities of pediatricians and mothers. To be sure, pregnancy and childbirth are intimate experiences for a woman. For nine months she provides all essential life support systems for the conceptus. She gives birth and she is biologically prepared to provide nourishment to her offspring. Developmentalists long have viewed infant care as an outgrowth of the mother's initial biological relationship to her conceptus and newborn. At the extreme was Margaret Mead's dictum that the father is "a biological necessity but a social accident." Thus father's role was conceptualized as that of family provider and companion to his wife, rather than as caregiver to his infant and young child.

Today, definition of the father's role in the family system is in transition. Results of intensive research during the past 15 years suggests that fathers can be important figures in the care of their infants. Prenatally, fathers may exert positive influences on the pregnant woman's emotional well-being. Fathers can assist in the childbirth process and there now are reasons to believe that they can provide for all aspects of infant care, excluding breast feeding. Fathers seem to be emotionally invested in their newborns, they form attachment relationships with their infants, and they contribute to the socialization process. In short, father's participation in infant care is a matter of performance, not of competence.

This is not to suggest that there are no differences in the caregiving skills of fathers and mothers, or that developmental consequences of increased father participation in infant care are known. In fact, no systematic data are available that would suggest specific developmental consequences for infants or for fathers in families in which fathers actively participate in caregiving. However, before the question of long term consequence is addressed, a great deal more must be learned about the immediate and short term effects of father participation in infant caregiving. The work included in this special issue draws attention to several aspects of fathers and infants: the father's role as a socializing agent, especially with respect to sex typing; activities that fathers engage in during the months after the infant's birth; and the father's interactions with infants who are at risk. A bibliography of over 500 references indicates that much research has been conducted with respect to father as caregiver, though the great proportion of these references deal with fathers and older children. Although much of the current issue focuses on empirical and theoretical issues, it should provoke considerable thought for application issues as well.

Our goal for this special issue was to bring fathers to the attention of infant specialists in a variety of disciplines which historically have placed great emphasis on the role of the mother in infant care and development. We hope the issue will stimulate empirical, theoretical, and applied work with fathers and their infants. To the extent that it does, our objective will be achieved.

Hiram E. Fitzgerald, PhD
Cathleen Erin McGreal, MA
Guest Editors

Infant Mental Health Journal, Vol. 2, No. 4, Winter 1981

The Father's Role in the Socialization of His Infant

Cathleen Erin McGreal, MA

ABSTRACT: Although research on fathers and infants increased dramatically during the past decade, it did so largely in a theoretical vacuum. Theories of development emphasize mother-infant relationships, with little attention, if any, given to father-infant relationships. As a result, studies of father-infant interactions tend to replicate procedures that have been used in mother-infant research. While useful, mimicking mother-infant research paradigms may blind investigators to salient aspects of development that are unique to and critical for father-infant relationships. In traditional families, study of mother-father-infant triadic interactions may reveal more useful information about the father's role in infant socialization, than the study of father-infant dyadic interactions. However, the study of triadic interactions may yield little useful information about father-infant interaction in the single parent family. Until a number of methodological issues are resolved, the literature on the father's role in the socialization of his infant must be interpreted cautiously.

It is fashionable for articles concerning the father's role in childrearing generally to begin by emphasizing the limited research attention that has been directed toward understanding the father's influence on infant development. However, there are a growing number of studies on father-infant relationships and fathers no longer can be thought of as "forgotten contributors to child development."[1] The purpose of this review is to evaluate current literature concerning the father's impact on the socialization of his infant, with particular emphasis placed on methodological problems which constrain interpretation of this literature.

Nearly all theories of development emphasize the importance of the maternal role for early social and personality development. This is especially true for the period of infancy, a time during which most theories stress the importance of the mother-infant feeding interaction. A comprehensive theory conceptualizing the role of the father during infancy has yet to be advanced. As a result it is often difficult to interpret research on the father and to integrate the finding of different investigations.

Cathleen E. McGreal is affiliated with the Department of Psychology, Michigan State University, in East Lansing, MI 48824.

0613-9641/81/1500-0216$00.95

Research on the father seems to be following a path similar to that of research on the mother. Early studies of the mother often focus on "maternal deprivation." As it became clear that studies of institutionalized infants yielded limited information on the role of the mother, emphasis shifted to controlled laboratory and direct observational studies of mother-infant interaction. Research on the role of the father in child development follows a similar pattern. The deficiency-oriented approach of examining homes with an absent father is being replaced by procedures involving father-present homes. Though in the first part of this shift fathers were studied via maternal reports, current studies favor direct observation of the father.

Several issues will be considered in terms of the father's contribution to infant socialization. Although fathers have been shown to be capable of performing caretaking functions there is little information concerning in which of these behaviors fathers commonly engage. It may be that adjustment of the man to fatherhood may depend more on commitment to a particular role in childrearing rather than the content of the role. Although research is being conducted which conceptualizes fatherhood as a crisis, this view does not seem to provide a useful framework for studying father-infant relationships. More normative data is needed on fathers' actual behaviors with their infants.

At the current time it is generally acknowledged that infants form attachments to their fathers as well as to their mothers. The importance of these attachments to the infant's development remains controversial. Several problems exist in this literature including conclusions that go beyond the data and inaccurate summarization of research. The complexity of studying father-infant and mother-infant relationships becomes apparent when one takes into consideration which parent acts as primary caregiver and which acts as secondary caregiver.

Research concerning the father's role in child development often lacks ecological validity. Since there is no theory to provide a working framework for research on the father, there is a tendency among researchers to replicate experimental procedures that have been derived from theoretical formulations of the maternal role in child development. Thus, even when fathers are studied directly, it is possible that salient aspects of their caregiving style are being overlooked. Pedersen and his associates[2] point out how subtle this problem can be. If a researcher controls for the size of a social group when making comparisons between mothers and fathers it may be that the data are not representative of both parents' typical experiences with their baby. Pedersen et al. found that when the father was the family's principal wage earner a two-person dyad, mother and infant, was the most characteristic social group for the mother, whereas a three-person group (father, mother, infant) was the most characteristic social unit for the father. Thus, one might justifiably study dyadic interactions in order to discover characteristics of mother-infant relationships. However, study of father-infant dyadic interactions may provide little ecologically valid information about the father's role as infant caregiver, regardless of the statistical significance of one's results.

A final area to be considered concerns the role of single fathers on the development of their children. At the present time there is little research on father-infant relationships in this area. However, given the number of marital separations in which infants are involved this is an important topic for further research.

THE FATHER'S CONTRIBUTION IN CARETAKING

Comparisons of fathers and mothers interacting with their newborn suggest differences in interactional style. For example, in one study fathers touched and vocalized to their babies just as often as mothers but held their babies more.[3] However, it is difficult to make any generalizations about the father's contribution during infancy from this study since the observation sessions occurred only one time for 10 minutes, and the presence of a female nurse as an observer may have altered interaction patterns considerably. Given the small size of many maternity rooms the addition of a second observer during 6 of these 19 sessions seems obtrusive. Active paternal involvement in terms of feeding sensitivity and nurturance has been reported in studies using similar experimental procedures.[4,5] Parke and Sawin[6] point out that these findings imply that fathers have the basic competence to effectively contribute to infant care. The father's competencies in this situation, however, reveal little information on the actual behaviors that may have impact on the child's social development.

It has been suggested that cultural support be provided for men so that fathers feel that caretaking responsibilities are consistent with their role and recognize themselves as being influential in the development of the child.[4] Fein,[7] however, found that effective postpartum adjustment on the part of the father was based on the development of a coherent role regardless of caretaking responsibilities. The fathers who saw themselves as ''breadwinners'' and those who saw themselves as ''nontraditional'' caretakers both adjusted effectively. Those having difficulty adjusting seemed uncertain over their role, wanting to be both caretakers and traditional providers. Commitment to a role, rather than the content of a particular role, may be the decisive factor in the father's adjustment to parenthood.

Recent literature also includes studies conceptualizing fatherhood as a crisis. Gilman and Knox[8] suggest that the father's means of coping should be considered before one makes any conclusions about what this crisis means in terms of the child. Their research is limited by the fact that since a crisis was assumed to be occurring, the procedure did not allow for its presence or absence to be confirmed. The authors state that use of an unsuccessful coping mechanism (fantasizing about prebaby days) leads to negative consequences for the baby, the father, and the marital relationship. The methodology of the study does not allow for any effects on the infant to be determined. Since 68% of those fathers using this unsuccessful coping mechanism rated their marital happiness as better than average this conceptualization does not seem useful.

Research has shown that adjustments certainly do occur to parenthood but the difficulties are not of crisis proportions even when 41% of the babies studied were born less than 9 months after marriage.[9] Given that this sample may have been more vulnerable to crisis than the more general population, the crisis oriented view of fatherhood does not seem a useful paradigm for studying the father's impact on the child's socialization. Specific explorations of high risk fathers and their infants[10] may provide more useful information concerning difficulties in father-infant relationships than would be obtained in a general framework in which fatherhood is viewed as a crisis.

In order to determine the father's role in socialization normative data are needed on the father's actual behaviors during infancy. The purposes of a recent investigation were to provide longitudinal data on the father's participation and to examine interactive aspects of father-child behavior.[11] During the neonatal period, data were collected on the father only if he happened to be home at the time of the observation. When the infant was 30 and 60 weeks of age *maternal reports* revealed that the most common father-infant activity was play and that the least common activities were bathing and changing. Feeding the baby and taking it out of the home became more frequent as the infant grew older. The indirect assessment of father-infant interactions seem inadequate given the purposes of the study.

Researchers also have investigated how much time is available for father-infant interaction. When parents were asked how much time each was with the child per day, mothers were reported to be present 6-10 hours and fathers 1-4 hours.[12] Kotelchuck[13] found that mothers were present 9 hours and fathers 3.2 hours per day. These figures may reveal physical presence with the child, but not interaction time. Observations of the father, mother and infant in the home showed a wide range (12%-84% of the observed time) of actual father involvement with the child.[14] The most common paternal activity involved watching the infant, followed by social participation and then play. Consideration of the infant's temperament revealed that fathers of "difficult" boys were more involved in social activities than were fathers of "difficult" girls. This points to the complexity involved in interactional research and the need for consideration of both members of the dyad.

In summary, there is limited information on father's actual behaviors in everyday interactions with their infants. Several studies suggest that the father's role as infant caregiver is limited by social-cultural factors affecting performance rather than by limitations in the father's competence to provide for optimal development.

THE FATHER AS AN ATTACHMENT FIGURE

The bulk of the current literature on the father involves studies of the infant's attachment to the father. As evidence against the concept of "monotropy" has accumulated, and the father has been acknowledged as an attachment figure, a debate has arisen over the importance of the father-infant relationship. Some researchers suggest that father-infant attachments do not make any unique contribution to the child's socialization. A review of infant attachments, for example, instructs the reader that the word "mother" is used to designate all those who have established a special relationship with the infant.[15] Proponents of the opposing view argue that the socializing performance of the nuclear family is probably due to the fact that mothers and fathers play such crucial and qualitatively different roles in socialization.[1] The available evidence, as cited below, provides no clear solution to this controversy. Under separation protest conditions, infants and toddlers react to both parents in a similar manner which is distinct from their reactions to strangers.[16,17] Problems exist, however, in defining these reactions as measures of attachment behaviors since children with high-interaction fathers show less behavior disruption when left alone with a stranger than low-father-interaction children.[18] Separation protest may be a reaction to a cognitively discrepant event rather than the display of an attachment.[19]

Much recent research focuses on mothers and fathers as elicitors of differential types of behavior such that proximal (or attachment) behaviors are directed to the mother and distal (or affiliative) behaviors are directed to the father. Conclusions based on this differentiation, however, go beyond the data. For example, after observing the free play behavior of one-year-olds, Ban and Lewis[20] concluded that infants do use different modes of expression in relating to each parent with father receiving distal modes of contact and mother receiving proximal contact. Their analysis does show more proximal contact to the mother. However, of the distal behaviors, more vocalizing was directed to the mother. Differences favoring the father in the other distal behavior, looking, were found only in boys. When the statistical significance found for vocalization is acknowledged the evidence does not support the proximal-distal dichotomy. A problem arises since in the same literature nonsignificant trends are used to support hypotheses concerning father-infant attachments. Lamb[21] reported that boys showed consistent, but nonsignificant preferences for their fathers on most of the free play measures while girls showed no preference. But in another article[22] he states that the previously cited study "drew attention to the fact that two-year-old boys show significant preferences for interaction with their fathers." Inaccurate summarization of other studies perpetuates the notion of a firm empirical base in an area of research that is still exploratory. Furthermore, when research is cited in later publications an impression is conveyed that the findings have been replicated several times. Although longitudinal investigations are very important in studying father-infant interaction, confidence in the *generalizability* of these results lessens when much of the research is based on the behaviors of the same babies.[23,24,25,26,27]

The goal of discovering qualitatively different behaviors for fathers and mothers may stem from the assumption that if one of the relationships is redundant then it has little significance for social-personality development.[26,27] Though relationships may be redundant at a global level, interindividual differences between parents could change the dynamics of the parent-child relationship. Attachments to more than one person may enhance the child's trust in the world. Observations of parents and infants in the home show that mothers usually had a greater quantity of interaction, but the quality remained similar for both parents.[28] The only exception to this was social play, in which the quantity of interaction was the same for mothers and fathers, but the quality differed. Play with the father was usually briefer, more physically involving and less often toy-mediated than play with the mother. The complexity involved in interpreting interactional differences is illustrated when the behaviors of primary caretaking mothers, primary caretaking fathers, and secondary caretaking fathers are examined.[29] During a play interaction, fathers, whether primary or secondary caretakers, held the infant's limbs less, played more games, and poked the infants more than mothers. Primary caretakers, both mothers and fathers, laughed less, smiled more, and made more imitative grimaces and high pitched vocalizations. Further research to differentiate between the behaviors of a primary vs. secondary caretaker and the behaviors of mothers and fathers is needed to assess the father's impact on socialization. A cross-lagged correlation of parents' verbal and play interactions, and childrens' intellectual development at 15, 20, and 30 months suggests a chain of influence such that mother influences child, child influences father and father influences mother.[28] This direction of causality, based on families with traditional role differentiation, implies an indirect paternal contribution. Before concluding that such is the case, investigations of both mothers and fathers acting as primary and secondary caretakers are needed.

ECOLOGICAL VALIDITY

Research on both the father and mother as attachment figures often lacks ecological validity. Bronfenbrenner[30] notes that research often treats the persons involved in a study as if they existed isolated from social contexts, and that when research does not concern experiences central to the life of the child only a partial picture of the child can be obtained. His point that much of American developmental psychology is actually the science of children's behaviors in strange situations with strangers is well taken as respects the literature of father-infant interactions. Replacing a baby at a "starting point" every minute[31] or having parents and strangers come and go for over 30 minutes,[17,18,21,23,24,25] may seem so frustrating or unusual to the infant that his/her reaction is not an accurate representation of how every day separations are handled. Experimental procedures may create situations that are unique rather than a regular part of the child's experience. For example, it is a common procedure to instruct parents to refrain from initiating any interaction during the observation, but to reciprocate when the child directs social behaviors towards them.[18,20,23,31] If this is an unusual behavior for the parent the dyadic interaction may reflect changes based on the instructions, and the observer views a distorted picture. Further distortion could occur if those in certain roles (e.g., mother-father; primary caregiver-secondary caregiver) usually initiate interactions more than those in the complementary roles. In natural observations in the home it was found that affiliative behaviors favored the mother especially where the action was parent-initiated.[28] However, the child was more responsive to father-initiated play than to mother-initiated play.

Recent investigations have looked at father-infant interactions in the home in order to determine which behaviors are more representative of their typical behaviors.[2,6,26,27,28,32,33,34] Convergent validation through home observation of findings obtained in the laboratory adds to the strength of the laboratory findings. For example, Belsky,[32] after observing parents (in the home) who were ''free to do as they pleased with no directives from the experimenter,'' found that his results agreed, in general, with those obtained in more manipulative studies. He suggests that the manipulative investigations may be providing an accurate picture of the family system after all. A combination of different research methods may be helpful in developing a clearer view of the father's role.

There also has been a trend toward greater ecological validity by consideration of the marital relationship as well as the parent-infant relationship. Pedersen[35] believes that a broader appreciation of the father's various roles within the family will develop once reseach questions are formulated ''beyond the 'fiction of convenience' that dyadic relationships exist in psychological isolation from other family members.'' When husband-wife interactions have been recorded during home observations it has been found that these interactions occur frequently when the parents are in the same room with their 5-month-old infant.[2] Furthermore, when communication between the spouses occurs, selective changes were observed not only in the parents' interactions with the baby but also in the baby's behavior.

SINGLE FATHERS

A final area of concern in the current literature involves the impact of the father on the socialization of his children after a marital separation. Since the emphasis is on single fatherhood, the ages of the children involved in these study vary. Information often is obtained through interviews with the father rather than observation of the father-child interaction and the data is often a retrospective account of the problems he encountered.[36] Problems in sample attrition also occur. A 2-year longitudinal study comparing interactions of divorced fathers to those of fathers in intact families reported that the sample was reduced from 144 families to 96 often because divorcees remarried and couples in the intact sample separated.[37] Paternal involvement (for fathers separated from their children) was found to decline over time even in men who had initially been highly involved with their children. Efforts to explore the role changes fathers encounter in adjusting to raising a child alone have emphasized home management chores and child rearing tasks rather than patterns of interactions.[38] Enjoyment of the paternal role is related to the reasons for becoming a single father.[39] Fathers' knowledge of normal child development was one factor relating to whether problems were occurring in the father-child relationship.[40]

CONCLUSIONS

In conclusion, research on the father is limited by the lack of a comprehensive theoretical formulation delineating his contribution to child development. Within the psychoanalytic tradition alone, current evaluation of the father's importance ranges from the view that his role is not to disturb the successful work of the mother[41] to the view that pre-oedipal father-child relationships are of considerable importance.[42] Recognition of the importance of both parents within one theoretical framework would lead to more systematic research efforts. Since studies of the father often utilize procedures that emerged from theoretical perspectives dealing with mother-child interaction, it may be that salient aspects of fathering have gone unexplored. In addition, though researchers are attempting to investigate mutual interaction patterns, theory regarding these reciprocal interaction patterns is minimal. Acknowledgement of the parent's processes of development, as well as the child's, would be useful. Also, there is a lack of integration between studies of fathers during infancy and studies of fathers during childhood. Attempts to bridge this gap would aid in understanding the father's role.

Research on both parents should expand beyond the current experimental paradigms. Besides physical settings (lab vs. home) attention should be given to the social or emotional context of the observation.[43] Study of parent-child dyads and family triads should be supplemented with the inclusion of others in the family and/or social network. Parke[5] suggests that in this manner the uniqueness of the father's role could be seen when contrasted to the role of other social figures that provide support for the mother.

In the past, mothers were usually a more accessible population than fathers and as such received more attention for practical, as well as theoretical, reasons. Since mothers are becoming less available for study, which equalizes the amount of effort required to study each parent, more researchers may be willing to study the father.

Sociobiological aspects of parenting should be included in conceptualizations of parent-child interactions. Statements that there are no predictable biological interactions involved in fathering,[44] are premature since there is little information available on the role of hormonal and physiological factors in mediating responses to infants and since it is possible that behavior changes hormonal levels.[5]

In recent years considerable attention has been devoted to exploration of the father's impact on socialization. Given the interest in fathering expressed by society and researchers alike, the future holds hope of a clearer description of the father's role in child development.

REFERENCES

1. Lamb ME: Fathers: Forgotten contributors to child development. *Human Dev 18*:245-266, 1975.
2. Pedersen FA, Anderson BJ, Cain RL, Jr.: Parent-infant and husband-wife interactions observed at age five months. In FA Pedersen (Ed), *The Father-Infant Relationship: Observational Studies in the Family Setting.* New York: Praeger, 1980.
3. Parke D, O'Leary SE, West S: Mother-father-newborn interaction: Effects of maternal medication, labor, and sex of infant. Proceedings, 80th Annual Convention, APA 85-86, 1972.
4. Parke RD, Sawin DB: The father's role in infancy: A re-evaluation. *Fam Coord 25*:365-371, 1976.
5. Parke, RD: Perspectives on father-infant interaction. In JD Osofsky (Ed). *Handbook of Infant Development.* New York: John Wiley and Sons, 549-590, 1979.
6. Parke RD, Sawin DB: The family in early infancy: Social interactional and attitudinal analyses. In FA Pedersen (Ed), *The Father-Infant Relationship: Observational Studies in the Family Setting.* New York: Praeger, 1980.
7. Fein RA: Men's entrance to parenthood. *Fam Coor 25*:341-348, 1976.
8. Gilman R, Knox D: Coping with fatherhood: the first year. *Child Psychiat Hum Dev 6*:134-148, 1976.
9. Hobbs DF, Wimbish JM: Transition to parenthood by black couples. *J Marr Fam 39*:677-689, 1977.
10. Bromberg P: Reaching high risk infant via their high risk fathers. *Infant Men Health J 1*:161-167, 1980.
11. Richards MPM, Dunn JF, Antonis B: Caretaking in the first year of life: The role of fathers, and mother's social isolation. *Child: Care, Health Dev 3*:23-36, 1977.
12. Fagot, BI: Sex differences in toddlers' behavior and parental reaction. *Dev Psych 10*:554-558, 1974.
13. Kotelchuck M: The infant's relationship to the father: Experimental evidence. In ME Lamb (Ed), *The Role of the Father in Child Development.* New York: John Wiley and Sons, 329-344, 1976.
14. Rendina I, Dickerscheid JD: Father involvement with first-born infants. *Fam Coor 25*:373-378, 1976.
15. Corter C: Infant attachments. In BM Foss (Ed), *New Perspective in Child Development.* Harmonsworth: Penguin, 1974.
16. Feldman SS, Ingham ME: Attachment behavior: A validation study in two age groups. *Child Dev 46*:319-330, 1975.
17. Ross G, Kagan J, Żelazo P, Kotelchuck M: Separation protest in infants in home and laboratory. *Dev Psych 11*:256-257, 1975.
18. Spelke E, Zelazo P, Kagan J, Kotelchuck M: Father interaction and seperation protest. *Dev Psych 9*:83-90, 1973.
19. Lester BM, Kotelchuck M, Spelke E, Sellers MJ, Klein RE: Seperation protest in Guatemalan infants: Cross cultural and cognitive findings. *Dev Psych 10*:79-80, 1974.
20. Ban PL, Lewis M: Mothers and fathers, girls and boys: Attachment behavior in the one-year-old. *Merrill-Palmer Q 20*:195-204, 1974.
21. Lamb ME: Interactions between two-year-olds and their mothers and fathers. *Psych Rep 38*:447-450, 1976.
22. Lamb ME: The sociability of two-year-olds with their mothers and fathers. *Child Psychiat Hum Dev 5*:182-188, 1975.
23. Lamb ME: Parent-infant interaction in eight-month-olds. *Child Psychiat Hum Dev 7*:56-63, 1976.
24. Lamb ME: Effects of stress and cohort on mother- and father-infant interaction. *Dev Psych 12*:435-443, 1976.
25. Lamb ME: Twelve-month-olds and their parents: Interaction in a laboratory playroom. *Dev Psych 12*:237-244, 1976.
26. Lamb ME: Father-infant and mother-infant interaction in the first year of life. *Child Dev 48*:167-181, 1977.
27. Lamb ME: The development of parent-infant attachments in the first two years of life. In FA Pedersen (Ed), *The Father-Infant Relationship: Observational Studies in the Family Setting.* New York: Praeger, 1980.
28. Clarke-Stewart KA: And daddy makes three: the father's impact on mother and young child. *Child Dev 49*:466-478, 1978.
29. Field T: Interaction behaviors of primary verus secondary caretaker fathers. *Dev Psych 14*:183-184, 1978.
30. Bronfenbrenner U: Developmental research, public policy, and the ecology of childhood. *Child Dev 45*:1-5, 1974.
31. Cohen LJ, Campos JJ: Father, mother, and stranger as elicitors of attachment behavior in infancy. *Dev Psych 10*:146-154, 1974.
32. Belsky J: Mother-father-infant interaction: A naturalistic observational study. *Dev Psych 15*:601-607, 1979.
33. Belsky J: A family analysis of parental influence on infant exploratory competence. In FA Pedersen (Ed), *The Father-Infant Relationship: Observational Studies in the Family Setting.* New York: Praeger, 1980.
34. Clarke-Stewart KA: The father's contribution to children's cognitive and social development in early childhood. In FA Pedersen (Ed), *The Father-Infant Relationship: Observational Studies in the Family Setting.* New York: Praeger, 1980.

35. Pedersen FA: Research issues related to fathers and infants. In FA Pedersen (Ed), *The Father-Infant Relationship: Observational Studies in the Family Setting.* New York: Praeger, 1980.

36. Keshet HF, Rosenthal KM: Fathering after marital separation. *Soc Work 23*:11-18, 1978

37. Hetherington, EM, Cox M, Cox R: Divorced fathers. *Fam Coord 25*:417-428, 1976.

38. Gasser RD, Taylor CM: Role adjustment of single parent fathers with dependent children. *Fam Coord 25*:397-401, 1976.

39. Mendes HA: Single fatherhood. *Soc Work 21*:308-312, 1976.

40. Mendes HA: Single fathers. *Fam Coord 25*:439-444, 1976.

41. Adler A: The child: Neither good nor evil. *J Individ Psychol 30:*191-193, 1974.

42. Machtlinger V: Psychoanalytic theory: Preoedipal and oedipal phases with special reference to the father. In ME Lamb (Ed), *The Role of the Father in Child Development.* New York: John Wiley and Sons, 277-305, 1976.

43. Falender CA, Mehrabian A: Environmental effects on parent-infant interaction. *Genet Psych Mon 97:*3-41, 1978.

44. Lewis M, Weinraub M: The father's role in the child's social network. In ME Lamb (Ed), *The Role of the Father in Child Development.* New York: John Wiley and Sons, 157-184, 1976.

Infant Mental Health Journal, Vol. 2, No. 4, Winter 1981

Sex-Typing in Infancy:
The Role of the Father

Thomas G. Power, PhD

ABSTRACT: Recent research on mother-infant interaction has provided little empirical support for the role of environmental factors in early sex-role development. In this paper, considerable support for the father's role is presented. Specifically, the research on mother- and father-infant interaction patterns is reviewed in order to describe developmental changes in the nature of differential treatment of the sexes during the first two years of life. Together, the studies reviewed highlight the importance of the father in early sex-role socialization, delineate a developmental model of the early differential treatment of the sexes, and provide clues as to the origins of later childhood sex differences in verbal and visual-spatial abilities.

SEX-TYPING IN INFANCY: THE ROLE OF THE FATHER

It has long been recognized that infant sex is a factor that can influence the nature of mother-infant interaction. Ever since Howard Moss carried out his first observations of mothers and infants in their homes,[1] researchers have set out to document the nature of early differential treatment of boy and girl infants. While the assumption behind much of this research was that it would have implications for understanding the process of early sex-role socialization, the results of most studies were not very encouraging: only a few studies suggested differential treatment of the sexes during the first 18 months of life. For example, of the 24 studies of mother-infant interaction reviewed for this paper that employed sample sizes of 20 or more healthy, full-term infants, only 16 considered infant sex as a factor and only 7 of these identified patterns of differential treatment (see Table 1). Furthermore, only 2 of the 15 studies published after 1975 reported differential treatment of boy and girl infants, and in both cases, the effects could be explained by a tendency for mothers to verbalize more to their girls than to their boys.[2,3]

In spite of this small number of significant findings, there is still much controversy about how the results of these studies should be interpreted. For

---

Dr. Power is an Assistant Professor in the Department of Psychology, University of Houston, Central Campus, Houston, TX 77004. Reprint requests may be addressed to him there.

0613-9641/81/1500-0226$00.95   *226*

Table 1

Studies of Mother-Infant Interaction

Study	Size	Infant Ages	Reported Sex Differences in Treatment + = yes, - = no, NA = no analyses reported
Period of Initial Adaptation			
Crockenberg & Smith, 2	54	newborn-3 mos.	+ (none after 1 mo.)
Moss, 1	30	newborn-3 mos.	+ (none after 3 wks.)
Thoman, Leiderman, & Olson, 14	40	newborn	+
Blehar, Lieberman, & Ainsworth, 15	26	6 wks.-15 wks.	-
Kaye, 16	30	newborn	-
Osofsky, 17	134	newborn	-
Osofsky & Danzger, 18	51	newborn	-
Dunn & Richards, 19	77	newborn-18 wks.	NA
Kaye & Fogel, 20	37	6 wks.-26 wks.	NA
Thoman, Turner, & Barnett, 21	44	newborn	NA
Period of Reciprocal Exchange			
Lewis, 22	32	3 mos.	+
Crawley et al., 23	48	4, 6, & 8 mos.	-
Lewis & Kreitzberg, 24	193	3 mos.	-
Period of Early Directed Activity			
Goldberg & Lewis, 25	64	6 mos.	+
Yarrow, Rubenstein, & Pederson, 26	41	5-6 mos.	+
Kaye, 27	91	6 mos.	-
Jennings et al., 28	60	6 mos.	NA

Table 1
(continued)

Study	Sample Size	Infant Ages	Reported Sex Differences in Treatment + = yes, - = no, NA = no analyses reported
Period of Focal- ization on the Parent			
Clarke-Stewart, 29	36	9-18 mos.	-
Messer, 30	42	11, 14, & 24 mos.	NA
Murphy & Messer, 31	24	9 & 14 mos.	NA
Period of Self- Assertion			
Schaffer & Crook, 3	24	15 & 24 mos.	+
Kendrick & Dunn, 32	40	18 & 43 mos.	-
Rubenstein & Howes, 33	30	17-20 mos.	NA
White & Watts, 34	39	12 & 24 mos.	NA

example, in reviews of the sex-typing literature, some theorists have argued that the studies with significant findings highlight the importance of early sex role socialization[4] while others have argued that since the majority of the studies show *no* significant differential treatment of the sexes, environmental factors must play a relatively minor role during the first 18 months of life. These theorists argue that 1) sex-role socialization probably does not begin until some time in the second or third year—once the child has begun to exhibit ''sex appropriate'' or ''sex inappropriate'' behavior, or 2) that biological and cognitive factors play a greater role than environmental factors in the process of early sex-role development.[5,6] Rarely have theorists argued for a strong psychobiological viewpoint[7] that stresses the interaction between biological factors and social cultural child-rearing practices.

Regardless of the interpretation one chooses, it is clear that these studies certainly do not provide *overwhelming* support for the role of environmental factors in early sex-role development. Before completely dismissing the importance of environmental factors, however, it is important to point out that in the research discussed thus far, at least one important environmental influence has not been examined: the influence of the father. Inasmuch as research with preschool and grade school children has indicated that fathers generally play a greater role in sex-typing than do mothers,[8,9,10] is likely that fathers may play a similar role during infancy. Certainly, an analysis of the degree to which father-infant interaction is influenced by infant sex appears necessary before any conclusions can be drawn about the role of early environmental factors in sex-role development. This is the purpose of the present review.

FATHERS AND SEX-TYPING: A DEVELOPMENTAL APPROACH

In sharp contrast to the data on mothers, fathers generally *do* treat their boys and girls differently. Significant patterns of differential treatment were identified in 14 of the 15 studies of father-infant interaction reviewed for this paper that employed sample sizes of 20 or more healthy, fullterm infants (see Table 2). Furthermore, differential treatment also was found in two studies

Table 2

Studies of Father-Infant Interaction

Study	Sample Size	Infant Ages	Reported Sex Differences in Treatment + = yes, - = no, NA = no analyses reported
Period of Initial Adaptation			
Parke & Sawin, 35	40	newborn to 3 mos.	+
Parke & O'Leary, 36: Study 1	19	newborn	+
Study 2	82	newborn	+
Period of Reciprocal Exchange			
Field, 37	36	4 mos.	+
Field, 38	60	4 mos.	+
Period of Early Directed Activity			
Lamb, 39	20	7 mos.	-
Power & Parke, 40 Study 1	24	8 mos.	+
Study 2	20	7 & 10 mos.	+
Rendina & Dicker-scheid, 41	40	7 & 13 mos.	+

Table 2
(continued)

Study	Sample Size	Infant Ages	Reported Sex Differences in Treatment + = yes, - = no, NA = no analyses reported
Toddlerhood			
Fagot, 46	24	20-24 mos.	+
Weinraub & Frankel, 47	40	18 mos.	+
Focalization on the Parent			
Power, 42	24	11, 14, 17 mos.	+
Period of Self-Assertion			
Belsky, 43	40	15 mos.	+
Lamb, 44	20	15-24 mos.	+
Smith & Danglish, 45	32	12 & 24 mos.	+

with smaller samples.[11,12] However, the patterns of differential treatment often varied with the infant's age. For example, differential treatment of newborn boys and girls differed considerably from the differential treatment of 18-month olds. Therefore, in the review that follows, data on the differential treatment of the sexes will be considered from a developmental perspective. Specifically, differences in the nature of father-son and father-daughter interactions during each of Sander's[13] 5 stages of mother-infant interaction will be discussed (see Table 3). In this way, it will be possible to specify developmental changes in the nature of early sex-role socialization and to speculate on the differential effects of sex-typing pressure at the different ages. In addition, data on both fathers *and* mothers will be presented and compared in order to present a more comprehensive picture of patterns of early sex-role socialization.

Period of Initial Adaptation (0 to 2½ Months)

The primary adaptive task during Sander's first period of mother-infant interaction involves the sensitive meshing of maternal activities with cues of the infant's state.[13] During this period the infant possesses a fairly limited social repertoire. Sensitive parenting involves learning to interpret and respond to the infant's signals of distress and interest, as well as providing the infant with an optimal level of early social stimulation in the form of looking, smiling, talking,

Table 3

Periods of Mother-Infant Interaction[a]

Period	Ages	Major Characteristics
Initial Adaptation	0-2 1/2 mos.	Meshing of mothering activities with cues of infant state
Reciprocal Exchange	2 1/2-5 mos.	Reciprocal face-to-face interactions; High level of positive affect
Early Directed Activity	5-9 mos.	Object centered interactions; Some infant-initiated interactions
Focalization on the Parent	9-12 mos.	Increased communicative competence; Intensification of "attachment" behavior; Many infant-initiated interactions
Self Assertion	12-18 mos.	Primarily brief, infant-initiated interactions; Beginnings of autonomy; Parent's "managerial" role

[a]Adapted from Sander (13)

and touching.[48] This is the period in which all parents learn about the idiosyncratic needs and characteristics of their new infant, and in which first-time parents learn about parenting and infants in general.

One might expect differential treatment of the sexes to be quite common during this period for at least two reasons. First, the only information initially available to parents concerning the unique characteristics of a healthy, full-term infant are its gender and its physical appearance. Therefore, one might expect that such characteristics may have a greater influence on parent behavior at this time than later in the first year after the parent has become familiar with aspects of the infants's temperament and other behavioral characteristics. This may be particulary true of parents of first-borns, since adults who have limited experience with infants may be more likely to believe that gender is a primary determinant of infant behavior.

A second reason why one might expect differential treatment of the sexes to be more likely during this intial period is that the young infant's limited social abilities require that patents initiate a disproportionate amount of their playful interactions with the child. This gives parents greater freedom in deciding when and how they interact with the infant, and thus may make differential treatment of the sexes more likely.

Data from studies of early mother-and father-infant interaction support the hypothesis that differential treatment of the sexes is common during this period. In the play and feeding interactions of newborn to 2-month-old infants and their parents, mothers and fathers show the same pattern of differential treatment; parents engage in more affectionate interactions with opposite-sexed infants and in more stimulating interactions with same-sexed infants. Specifically, mothers spend more time breastfeeding and holding close their sons[14,35] and more time looking at, talking to, smiling at and touching their daughters.[2,14,35,36] Fathers spend more time holding their daughters close[35] and more time looking at, talking to, touching, and showing toys to their sons. However, in *unstructured* interaction sessions during the early weeks, mothers spend more *overall* time interacting with their boys.[1,2] This appears to be related to the lower level of alertness and greater level of irritability found in boys: mothers spend more time overall with their boys than with their girls, but primarily because fussy boys require more caretaking.[1,2] However, when mothers *do* interact in the caretaking context, they are more likely to accompany the routine caretaking of their girls with visual, verbal, or physical stimulation. Data regarding the overall amount of interaction for fathers are not available during this time period. Finally, all of the patterns of differential treatment discussed above are much more characteristic of parents of first-born than parents of later-born infants.[2,24,36]

Period of Reciprocal Exchange (2½ to 5 Months)

Sander's second period of mother-infant interaction is characterized by reciprocal, affectively charged, face-to-face interactions between mothers and infants. Such interactions have been the focus of much research on early mother-infant communication,[49] but few of these studies have indentified patterns of differential treatment of the sexes (see Table 1). In two studies that followed samples of infants from the first through the third months of life,[1,2] the majority of differences found in the early period had disappeared by the time the infants were 3 months of age. An exception concerned verbal interactions: mothers of 3-month-olds were more likely to vocalize to and imitate the vocalizations of their daughters.[1,22]

In contrast, fathers continue to show differential treatment of the sexes at 3 months of age. Field found that fathers of full term infants played more interactive games with their boys than with their girls[37,38] and that these fathers, like mothers, were more likely to imitate their girl's vocalizations.[37] In addition, the pattern of differential treatment of the sexes by fathers identified by Parke and Sawin[35] in the newborn period and at 3 weeks was also significant at 3 months.

Together, these findings support the hypotheses presented above. As predicted, differential treatment of the sexes was more likely to occur during the infant's first few weeks of life than in the later months. This appears to be true, however, only for mothers. Fathers continue to show patterns of differential treatment throughout both time periods.

This difference between mothers and fathers can be accounted for by a number of attitudinal, perceptual and experiential factors. First, a number of studies have shown that fathers are more likely than mothers to report sex-differences in their child-rearing goals, especially in the area of achievement motivation.[50,51] Therefore, fathers may continue to treat the sexes differently because they view sex-typing as an important part of their role as father. Second, fathers are more likely than mothers to have sex-stereotyped perceptions of their infant's behavior.[52] This could also result in the continuing pattern of differential treatment if indeed sex-stereotyped perceptions result in sex-typed behavior. Finally, mother-father differences in experience with the infant may also play a role. Specifically, as a result of their more limited involvement with their infants, fathers, in comparison to mothers, may develop less sensitivity to their infant's behavioral signals and therefore continue to be more influenced by obvious physical characteristics of the infant (such as gender or physical appearance) than by more subtle behavioral cues. This would result in mother-father differences in treatment only if these physical characteristics are not highly correlated with individual differences in infant behavior.

While few studies have *directly* assessed the relative importance of infant physical vs. behavioral characteristics on parent-infant interaction patterns, some suggestive evidence is available. Hildebrant,[53] in a study of the relationship between infant physical attractiveness and the face-to-face interaction of parents and their 3 month old infants, found that fathers directed more positive social behaviors toward more attractive infants while mothers directed more social behaviors toward *less* attractive infants. In interpreting these findings, she writes:

> Since the fathers in this study spent less time caring for their infants than the mothers did, it might be expected that they would be positively influenced by an immediately obvious cue such as physical attractiveness. The mothers, on the other hand, may have been equally aware of their infant's attractiveness. However, rather than simply reacting to the infant on the basis of attractiveness, they may have tried to make their less cute infants appear cuter by attempting to elicit more social behaviors from them.

Support for the hypothesis that fathers are less influenced by infant behavior during the course of parent-infant interactions comes from Power's[54] study of parent-infant play. In this study, parents and their 8-month-old infants were videotaped in a 20-minute laboratory play session while playing with some toys. The findings relevant here concerned the differences in how mothers and fathers reacted when their infant showed signs of disinterest in playing with a particular toy. Whereas mothers reacted to these signs of disinterest by shifting the focus of their play to the new toy that the infant had become interested in, fathers were more likely to ignore the new object of interest and engage in physical play. In addition, when fathers *did* initiate play with toys, they were more likely than mothers to be unsuccessful in getting the infant interested in the toy because the infant was already playing with a *different* toy. In short, mothers were more likely than fathers to gear carefully the focus of their toy play interactions to their infant's subtle behavioral cues of interest and disinterest. Clearly, more studies of the relationships between infant physical characteristics, infant behavioral characteristics, and parent-infant interaction styles are necessary in order to test more directly this final hypothesis.

Period of Early Directed Activity (5 to 9 Months)

In Sander's third stage of mother-infant interaction, the infant begins to play a greater role in initiating social interactions with the parent. Although these initiations are often very simple in nature (looks at parent, crawls to parent, etc.), they do represent the infant's early attempts to pull the parent into play. An even greater difference between parent-infant interactions in this stage compared to interactions in the previous stage concerns the role of objects. Since this stage covers a period of rapid locomotor and fine motor development (the infant changes from an immobile child who can barely grasp objects to one who can creep, crawl, and manipulate virtually everything in reach), the infant spends the vast majority of its time manually exploring an environment that was previously only available for visual inspection. Not surprisingly, this means that most of the parent-infant interactions that occur during this period are object-centered.

A recent study by Ricks and associates[55] highlights this change. In their cross-sectional study of face-to-face interaction between mothers and infants at 3, 6, and 9 months of age, these investigators found that by 6 and particularly by 9 months of age, the primary form of play observed was object-focused play- although the mothers were instructed not to play with objects and no play objects were made available. Surprisingly, the infant's interest in objects was so strong during the 6 and 9 month time points that fingers, feet, and the strap of the infant seat became the primary focus of these interactions.

As was the case in the last peroid, studies of mother-infant interaction during the period of early directed activity show few significant patterns of differential treatment of the sexes. The only consistent exception involves vocal behavior: mothers generally vocalize more often and use more diverse speech with their daughters.[25,26]

Fathers continue to show differential treatment of the sexes in a number of ways. For example, in their naturalistic home observations of fathers with their 7-month-old infants, Rendina and Dickerscheid[41] found that fathers spent more time looking at and playing with their sons than with their daughters. Moreover, in two recent studies of mother-and father-infant interaction, Power and Parke[40] found other differences in treatment. In the first study, the laboratory study of mother-and father infant play briefly discussed in the previous section,[40,54] fathers of first-born, 8-month-old boys engaged in more intense, physical play than did fathers of first-born 8-month-old girls. In the second study, an observational study of mother-father-infant interaction in the home, fathers of first-born, 7- and 10-month-old infants were more likely to encourage visual, locomotor, and fine motor exploration in boys, while they encouraged vocal behavior in girls. Mothers showed no differential treatment of the sexes.

Period of Focalization on the Parent (9 to 12 Months)

Sander's next stage, the period of focalization on the parent, coincides with a number of significant developments in the infant's ability to initiate social interactions. During this period, the infant develops a number of social skills that greatly expand its initiating repertoire. These skills include such diverse behaviors as socially directed vocalizations,[57,58] pointing,[59,60] showing, and giving.[61] An important characteristic of this period "concerns the extension of initiative in the child to achieve something of a manipulation of the mother, especially a focalization on her as a person who meets his needs" (p. 142).[13] So, not only do infants develop a number of new ways to influence adult behavior during this period, they become more likely to direct these behaviors toward parents or significant others. In other words, this is a period of the intensification of "attachment" behavior[48] and in contrast to the previous periods, a time characterized by a large number of infant-initiated parent-infant interactions.

In light of the numerous infant social and communicative developments that occur, it is surprising that this peroid has been focus of so few studies of parent-infant interaction (see Tables 1 and 2). Although Table 1 lists 3 studies of mother-infant interaction during the period of focalization on the parent, only one of these studies investigated the nature of naturally occurring mother-infant interactions in the home.[29]

As was the case in the last two periods, only fathers show differential treatment of the sexes during this period.[40,42] Power and Parke[40] found that fathers of 10-month-olds showed the same pattern of differential treatment that characterized fathers of 7-month-olds: fathers encouraged visual, fine motor, and locomotor exploration in their boys and vocal behavior in their girls. Moreover, a larger follow-up study[42] of some of the same families who had participated in the Power and Parke home study [40] continued to identify differential treatment of the sexes by fathers at 11, 14, and 17 months. However, the pattern of differential treatment of 11-month-olds more closely resembled the ways in which fathers interacted with their 14- and 17-month-olds than it resembled interactions between fathers and their 7- or 10-month-olds. Thus sometime during the tenth or eleventh month of life, a significant change in the nature of differential treatment of the sexes occurred. In order to understand this change, we must turn to a discussion of the studies involving 12- to 18-month-olds encompassing Sander's final period, the "period of self assertion."

The Period of Self-Assertion (12 to 18 Months)

During Sander's final period of mother-infant interaction, the primary issue is the development of autonomy. As the infant begins to walk and more actively explore the physical environment, parent-infant interactions come more and more under the infant's control. For example, White and associates[62] found that over 85% of the time, 12- to 33-month-old infants initiated their own activities. Thus, during this period, parents begin to shift from the role of "stimulator" into a more "managerial" role.[40] The parent spends less time engaged in extended interactions with the infant, and more time organizing and arranging the infant's home environment, and setting boundaries on the range of the home setting to which the child has access.[40,63]

Differences in the treatment of the sexes parallel this shift from the "stimulation" to "managerial" role. For example, both Power[42] and Smith and Danglish[45] found that parents showed no differential treatment of the sexes in terms of the direct encouragement of exploratory behavior during this period, but that both mothers and fathers were more likely to allow their sons to explore on their own and less likely to restrict their sons from engaging in various kinds of "forbidden play" (the manipulation of breakable objects, etc.). When differences concerning the role of the stimulator *do* occur, most studies show that these differences in treatment generally involve social behaviors. For example, during this period mothers are more likely to vocalize and use more diverse speech with their girls than with their boys,[3,44,47,56] whereas fathers spend more time watching,[41] playing with,[41,47] kissing and hugging,[43] and talking to[44] their boys and more time trying to get their girls to vocalize and to share.[42] Thus, in comparison to the previous period, the period of self assertion is a time when differential treatment of the sexes is evident in both the stimulation and managerial roles.

Toddlerhood (18 to 24 Months)

The final period to be considered in this review is the second half of the infant's second year of life. Although this period was not considered by Sander, it is the first period in which children spend much of their time involved in what might be termed "sex-appropriate" and "sex-inappropriate" activities. During this period, the child's developing language, cognitive, and motor abilities enable him or her to engage in activities that parents may consider to be appropriate or inappropriate for a particular sex. Examples of "appropriate" behaviors include running, jumping, and fighting for boys, and role-playing and dependency (i.e., asking for help) for girls. Moreover, since toys that are designed for toddlers can be more readily classified by parents as being "male" or "female" toys (transportation toys, blocks, dolls, soft toys, etc.), the toys available to children during this period might also increase the likelihood of differential treatment of the sexes.

A recent study by Fagot[46] clearly shows that differential treatment of boys and girls is common during this period. In this naturalistic study of parent-toddler interaction, mothers and fathers of 20-to 24-month-old children were observed during 5 sixty-minute observation sessions in their homes. During these sessions, observers coded parental reactions to a large number of child behaviors. The results indicated that parents generally responded positively to "sex-appropriate" behaviors and negatively to "sex-inappropriate" behaviors. For example, while mothers and fathers responded positively when their boys played with transportation toys, push toys, and blocks or when their girls played with soft toys and dolls, parents responded negatively when their boys played with soft toys or dolls. In addition, while mothers and fathers responded positively if their girls watched television, followed the parent around, asked for help or helped the parent engage in an activity, they responded negatively if their boys helped or asked for help, or if their girls engaged in running, jumping, or climbing play. Fathers were more likely to show these patterns of differential treatment in three of the four cases where one parent showed significantly greater differential treatment in the sexes than the other. No significant mother-father differences were found for the remaining behaviors. Thus, while fathers are generally the parents who engage in differential treatment of the sexes during the first 18 months of life, the results of this study indicate that mothers may begin to play a greater role in this regard toward the end of the second year.

SUMMARY AND CONCLUSIONS

Together, the studies reviewed above suggest a developmental pattern of the differential parenting of male and female infants. Whereas fathers engage in differential treatment of the sexes throughout the first eighteen months of life, mothers, with one exception—the encouragement of vocal behavior in girls— only show differential treatment during the newborn period. Thus, while both mothers and fathers tend to be influenced by their infant's sex directly after the birth (at a time when little information about the infant's behavioral characteristics or abilities are available), only fathers continue to show differential treatment after this period. Three factors that may account for this pattern of results were discussed: 1) fathers show more sex differentiation in their child-rearing goals than do mothers, 2) fathers' perception of their infant's behavior are more easily influenced by infant sex, and 3) certain mother-father differences in sensitivity to infant cues appear to play an important role.

This review also suggests a description of the *nature* of fathers' early differential treatment of the sexes: while fathers actively encourage the development of manipulatory and visual-spatial abilities in their boys, they generally encourage the development of verbal abilities in their girls. Specifically, regardless of the infant's age, fathers spend much of their time encouraging their boys to explore and play with objects, while they encourage their girls to vocalize. However, the *ways* in which they encourage these behaviors vary with the infant's developmental status. For example, fathers encourage exploratory skills in their boys first by showing them toys (newborn to 3 months), then by encouraging the manipulation of toys (7 to 10 months), and finally by allowing them to explore freely the physical environment on their own (11 to 17 months). Similarly, while fathers of 3-month-old girls encourage vocal behavior through imitating games, fathers of older girl infants are more likely to encourage vocal behavior through asking questions and labelling objects. It is likely that this differential encouragement of exploratory and vocal behaviors in boy and girl infants may have implications for understanding the origins of later childhood sex differences in verbal and visual-spatial abilities.

Finally, after eighteen months of age, both fathers *and* mothers appear to play an important role in sex-typing. This may be related to the child's developing ability to engage in interactions that parents may perceive as being "sex-appropriate" or "sex-inappropriate".

While these studies provide some hypotheses concerning the mother's and the father's role in early sex-role socialization, they also highlight the need for further research in this area. Two kinds of studies need to be carried out. First, since there have been few descriptive studies of mother-and father-infant interaction during Sander's[13] last two periods of parent-infant interaction, future research with infants between the ages of nine and twenty-four months is necessary in order to replicate and validate the developmental hypotheses presented above. Second, the developmental importance of these early parent-infant interaction patterns needs to be verified through studies designed to investigate the relationship between the early differential treatment of the sexes and later individual differences in sex-role development. Only in this way can the importance of experiential factors in sex-role development be more clearly established.

REFERENCES

1. Moss H: Sex, age, and state as determinants of mother-infant interaciton. *Merrill-Palmer Quart 13*: 19-36, 1967.
2. Crockenberg S, Smith P: Antecedents of mother-infant interaction and infant irritability in the first three months of life. Paper presented at the International Conference on Infant Studies, New Haven, CT, 1980.
3. Schaffer H, Crook C: Maternal control techniques in a directed play situation. *Child Dev 50*:989-996, 1979.
4. Birns B: The emergence and socialization of sex differences in the earliest years. *Merrill-Palmer Quart 22*:229-254, 1976.
5. Lewis M, Weinraub M: Origins of early sex-role development. *Sex Roles 5*: 135-153, 1979.
6. Maccoby E, Jacklin C: *The Psychology of Sex Differences.* Stanford, Stanford University Press, 1974.
7. Fitzgerald HE: Infants and caregivers: Sex differences as determinants of socialization. In E Donelson and J Gullahorn (Eds), *Women: A Psychological Perspective.* New York, John Wiley, 1976.
8. Goodenough E: Interest in persons as an aspect of sex difference in the early years. *Genet Psych Mon 55*: 287-323, 1957.
9. Johnson M: Sex role learning in the nuclear family. *Child Dev 34*: 315-333, 1963.
10. Sears R, Maccoby E, Levin H: *Patterns of Child Rearing.* Evanston IL, Row Peterson, 1957.
11. Fagot B: Sex differences in toddler's behavior and parental reaction. *Dev Psych 10*: 554-558, 1974.
12. Rebelsky F, Hanks C: Father's verbal interaction with infants in the first three months of life. *Child Dev 42*: 63-68, 1971.
13. Sander L: Issues in early mother-child interaction. *J Am Acad Child Psychiat 1*:141-166, 1962.
14. Thoman E, Leiderman H, Olson P: Neonate-mother interaction during breastfeeding. *Dev Psych 6*:110-118, 1972.
15. Blehar M, Lieberman A, Ainsworth M: Early face-to-face interaction and its relations to later infant-mother attachment. *Child Dev. 48*:182-194, 1977.
16. Kaye K: Toward the origin of dialogue. In H Schaffer (Ed), *Studies in Mother-Infant Interaction.* London, Academic Press, 1977.
17. Osofsky J: Neonatal characteristics and mother-infant interaction in two observational situations. *Child Dev 47*:1138-1147,1976.
18. Osofsky J, Danzger B: Relationships between neonatal characteristics and mother-infant characteristics. *Dev Psych 10*:124-130, 1974.
19. Dunn J, Richards M: Observations on the developing relationship between mother and baby in the neonatal period. In H Schaffer (Ed), *Studies in Mother-Infant Interaction.* London, Academic Press, 1977.

20. Kaye K, Fogel A: The temporal structure of face-to-face communication between mothers and infants. *Dev Psych 16*:454-464, 1980.
21. Thoman E, Turner A, Leiderman P, Barnett C: Neonate-mother interaction: effects of parity on feeding behavior. *Child Dev 41*:1103-1111, 1970.
22. Lewis M: State as an infant-environment interaction: An analysis of mother-infant behavior as a function of sex. *Merrill-Palmer Quart 18*:95-121, 1972.
23. Crawley S, Rogers P. Friedman S, Iacobbo M, Critics A, Richardson L, Thompson M: Developmental changes in the structure of mother-infant play. *Dev Psych 14*:30-36, 1978.
24. Lewis M, Kreitzberg V: Effects of birth order and spacing on mother-infant interactions. *Dev Psych 15*:617-625, 1979.
25. Goldberg S, Lewis M: Play behavior in the year-old infant: Early sex differences. *Child Dev 40*:21-31, 1969.
26. Yarrow L, Rubenstein J, Pedersen F: *Infant and Environment: Early Cognitive and Motivational Development.* New York, Halsted, 1975.
27. Kaye K: Infant's effects upon their mother's teaching strategies. In Glifewell (Ed), *The Social Context of Learning and Development.* New York, Gardner, 1976.
28. Jennings K, Harmon R, Morgan G, Gaiter J, Yarrow L: Exploratory play as an index of mastery motivation: Relationships to persistence, cognitive functioning, and environmental measures. *Dev Psych 15*:386-394, 1979.
29. Clarke-Stewart K: Interactions between mothers and their young children: Characteristics and consequences. *Monographs of the Society for Research in Child Development 38*:(6-7 Ser. 153), 1973.
30. Messer D: The integration of mother's referential speech with joint play. *Child Dev 49*:781-787, 1978.
31. Murphy C, Meser D: Mothers, infants and pointing: A study of a gesture. In H Schaffer (Ed), *Studies in Mother-Infant Interaction.* London, Academic Press, 1977.
32. Kendrick C, Dunn J: Caring for a second baby: Effects on interaction between mother and firstborn. *Dev Psych 16*:303-311, 1980
33. Rubenstein J, Howes C: Caregiving and infant behavior in day care and in homes. *Dev Psych 15*:1-24, 1979.
34. White B, Watts J: *Experience and Environment.* Englewood Cliffs, Prentice Hall, 1973.
35. Parke R, Sawin D: The family in early infancy: Social interactional and attitudinal analyses. In F Pedersen (Ed), *The Father-Infant Relationship: Observational Studies in the Family Setting.* New York, Praeger, 1980.
36. Parke R, O'Leary S: Father-mother-infant interaction in the newborn period: Some feelings, observations, and some unresolved issues. In K Riegal and J Meacham (Eds), *The Developing Individual in a Changing World*(Vol 2) *Social and Environmental Issues.* The Hague, Mauton, 1975.
37. Field T: Interaction patterns of primary versus secondary caretaker fathers. *Dev Psych 14*:183-185, 1978.
38. Field T: Games parents play with normal and high-risk infants. *Child Psychiat Hum Dev 10*:41-48, 1979.
39. Lamb M: Father-infant and mother-infant interaction in the first year of life. *Child Dev 48*:167-181, 1977.
40. Power T, Parke R: Play as a context for early learning: Lab and home analyses. In I Sigel and L Laosa (Eds), *The Family as a Learning Environment.* New York, Plenum, in press.
41. Rendina I, Dickerscheid J: Father involvement with first-born infants. *Fam Coord 25*:373-379, 1976.
42. Power T: Patterns of early infant socialization: A descriptive analysis of mother- and father-infant interaction in the home. Unpublished Doctoral Dissertation, University of Illinois, 1980.
43. Belsky J: Mother-father-infant interaction: A naturalistic observational study. *Dev Psych 15*:601-607, 1979.
44. Lamb M: The development of mother-infant and father-infant attachments in the second year of life. *Dev Psych 13*:639-649, 1977.
45. Smith P, Daglish L: Sex differences in parent and infant behavior in the home. *Child Dev 48*:1250-1254, 1977
46. Fagot B: Sex determined parental reinforcing contingencies in toddler children. Paper presented at the biennial meeting of the Society for Researach in Child Development, New Orleans, LA, 1977.
47. Weinraub M, Frankel J: Sex differences in parent-infant interaction during free play, departure, and separation. *Child Dev 48*:1240-1249, 1977.
48. Ainsworth M, Blehar M, Waters E, Wall S: *Strange Situation Behavior of One-Year-Olds.* New York, Lawrence Erlbaum, 1978.
49. Stern D: *The First Relationship: Infant and Mother.* Cambridge, Mass, Harvard University Press, 1977.
50. Hoffman L: Changes in family roles, socialization, and sex differences. *Am Psych 32*:644-657, 1977.
51. Katz L, Bowermaster J, Jacobson E, Kessell L: *Sex Role Socialization in Early Childhood.* Urbana, IL, ERIC Clearinghouse on Early Childhood Education, 1977.
52. Rubin J, Provenzano F, Lurin Z: The eye of the beholder: Parents' views on sex of newborns. *Am J Orthopsychiat 43*:720-731, 1974.
53. Hildebrandt K: Parents' perceptions of their infants' physical attractiveness. Paper presented at the International Conference on Infant Studies, New Haven, CT, 1980.

54. Power T: Mother- and father-infant play: An exploratory analysis of structure and function. Unpublished Master's Thesis, University of Illinois, 1980.
55. Ricks M, Krafchuk E, Tronick E: A descriptive study of mother-infant interaction at 3, 6, and 9 months of age. Paper presented at the biennial meeting of the Society for Research in Child Development, San Francisco, CA, 1979.
56. Phillips J: Syntax and vocabulary of mother's speech to young children: Age and sex comparisons. *Child Dev 44*:182-185, 1973.
57. Bates E, Camaioni L, Volterra V: The acquisition of performatives prior to speech. *Merrill-Palmer Quart 21*:205-226, 1975.
58. Harding C, Golinkoff R: The origins of intentional vocalizations in prelinguistic infants. *Child Dev 50*:33-40, 1979.
59. Murphy C: Pointing in the context of a shared activity. *Child Dev 49*:371-380, 1978.
60. Leung E, Rheingold H: The development of pointing as a social gesture. Unpublished manuscript, University of North Carolina at Chapel Hill, 1979.
61. Rheingold H, Hay D, West M: Sharing in the second year of life. *Child Dev 47*:1148-1158, 1976.
62. White B, Kaban B, Shapiro B, Attonucci J: Competence and experience. In I Uzgiris and F Weizmann (Eds), *The Structuring of Experience*. New York, Plenum Press, 1976.
63. Parke R: Children's home environments: Social and cognitive effects. In I Altman and J Wohlwill (Eds), *Children and the Environment*(Vol 3) *Human Behavior and Environment*. New York, Plenum Press, 1978.

Infant Mental Health Journal, Vol. 2, No. 4, Winter 1981

Games Fathers and Mothers Play with Their Infants

Michael W. Yogman, MD

ABSTRACT: Both fathers and mothers successfully engaged their infants one to six months of age in interactive games in a laboratory play situation. Both parents played almost one game per minute with their infants. Mother played more conventional limb movement games and more distal, visual, attention maintaining games while fathers played more proximal, arousing, idiosyncratic limb movement games with their infants. Interactive games with parents even during the first six months of infancy provide differential experiences for the infant. These games may have developmental significance in selectively facilitating the acquisition of social and cognitive skills.

Recent studies of parent-infant social interaction have demonstrated that fathers as well as mothers can establish a direct social relationship with their infants. Father's sensitivity as a social interactant[1, 2] and his salience as an attachment figure[3, 4] with his infant has been well-documented. Attention now is focused on specifying the qualitative and structural aspects of father-infant interaction in order to understand the ways in which father and infant influence each other.

Play appears to be a useful context within which to study the influences of parents and infants on each other. Play between parents and infants is not only a pleasurable social activity but may also be the context in which a large number of social and cognitive skills are learned.[5] Play between mothers and young infants has been extensively described and analyzed[6,7] and studies of play between fathers and older infants (8-30 months of age) have suggested differences in the amount and kinds of play fathers and mothers engage in with their infants: fathers engaging in more physical, idiosyncratic play and mothers engaging in more conventional play.[3, 8] In this paper, play between fathers and young infants (1-6 months of age) was studied and compared with play

---

Dr. Yogman is Associate Chief of the Child Development Unit, Children's Hospital Medical Center, 300 Longwood Avenue, Boston, MA 02115 and the Harvard Medical School. The support of the Robert Wood Johnson Foundation, the Carnegie Corporation and the National Institute of Mental Health is gratefully acknowledged. An extended version of this work will be published in *Theory and Research in Behavioral Pediatrics,* Vol. 1, New York: Plenum Press (H E Fitzgerald, B M Lester and M W Yogman, (Eds).

0613-9641/81/1500-0241$00.95   *241*

between mothers and young infants. Specific behavioral subunits of play labelled "games" are the focus of this paper.

METHOD

Subjects

Six first-born infants (three females and three males) and their mothers and fathers were recruited in the newborn period, and studied longitudinally during the first 6 months of life. Mothers were the primary caretakers in all families. Infants were all healthy, full-term, appropriate birth weight for gestational age, and were delivered after uncomplicated pregnancies.

Procedure

The method for eliciting and studying parent-infant play involved videotaping the face-to-face play of parents and infants in a laboratory.[9] Since no toys were available, this method placed maximal demands on the social capabilities of the participants and enabled us to elicit and study in a detailed way specific subunits of play called "games".

Each infant was studied during interaction with each parent in the laboratory. Two minute periods of play were videotaped with both mother and father, separated by 30 seconds of infant alone to be sure that she or he was alert. Parents waited outside the laboratory when not interacting with their infant. The infant, when alert and calm, was seated in an infant seat placed on a table surrounded by curtains. The adult entered from behind the curtain, sat in front of the infant and was instructed to "play without using toys and without removing the infant from the seat." The order in which parents interacted with their infant was counterbalanced. One video camera focused on the infant, the other on the adult. The two images appeared simultaneously on a split screen monitor (Figure 1) which showed a single frontal view of adult and infant along with a digital time display. Sound was recorded simultaneously.

Coding

Nine sessions were recorded for each infant with his/her mother and father at 4, 6, 8, 10, 12, 14, 16, 20 and 24 weeks of age. Within the overall two minute play period, specific episodes occurred which were referred to as games. Games as defined by Stern are: "A series of episodes of mutual attention in which the adult uses a repeating set of behaviors with only minor variations during each episode of mutual attention."[6] For example, games included such parental activities as verbally imitating the baby's "coss" in a turn-taking fashion; exercising an infant in a "pull-to-sit" game; repeatedly tapping the baby at corners of the mouth (see Figure 1); and conducting the baby's arms while singing to her (see Figure 2).

All videotapes were reviewed in order to describe the components of these games. Each episode that met the definition of a game was described in detailed narrative form. In a second step, descriptions of the games were then categorized according to a system devised by Crawley, et al.,[7] which was modified for this study. Gross body movement games were omitted since the use of the infant seat precluded their occurrence. Pure verbal games were added to the list of categories. Definitions and sample descriptions of the games are shown in Table 1.

All games were categorized into one of the seven categories: tactile, limb movement, conventional limb movement, visual, conventional visual, combination, and pure verbal. Limb movement games and conventional limb movement games were those in which the parent moved the infant's limbs in space. If the limb movement game was characterized by a traditional motoric role assumed by the infant (e.g., pat-a-cake, clapping, peek-a-boo), it was categorized as a conventional limb movement game. If the limb movement game lacked a traditional motoric-role (e.g., parent simply shakes infant's arms), it was labelled a limb movement game. Visual games and conventional visual games occurred when the parent provided distal

Figure 1. Father and infant (4 weeks) playing "tapping" game.

stimulation in terms of motor movements that were visually observed by the infant. If the parent demonstrated traditional motor activities such as pat-a-cake, peek-a-boo, or clapping, the game was labelled a conventional visual game. If the motor activities were not traditional (e.g., parent wiggles fingers in front of infant), the game was labelled a visual game.

RESULTS

Results can be seen in Table 2. Games occurred during most sessions, and were somewhat more likely to occur during sessions with fathers than with mothers. Mothers and infants played games during 75% of the 54 sessions, while fathers and infants played games during 87% of the sessions. Parents usually played more than one game per session (mean for mothers = 1.7 games/session; mean for fathers = 1.65 games/session). Of the games that did occur, pure tactile and pure verbal games and combinations of the two were quite common with both parents. Visual games in which the parent displays distal motor movements that may be observed by the infant and appear to be attempts to maintain the visual attention of the infant also were quite common whether or not accompanied by verbal games. These visual games were more common with mothers than with fathers. They represented the most common

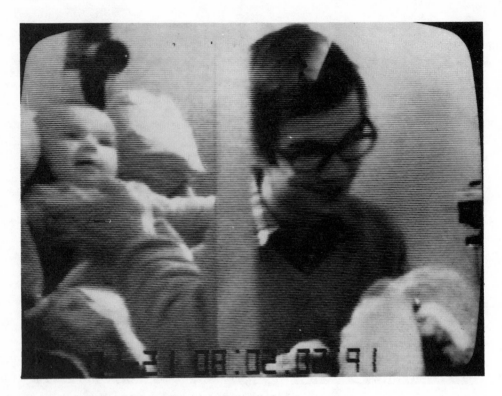

Figure 2. Father and infant (12 weeks) playing limb movement game.

mother-infant games (36% of all games played) and occurred in 46% of all mother-infant sessions (61% of sessions in which any games occurred). With fathers, these games represented only 20% of all games played, significantly lower than with mothers.

The most common type of father-infant games were tactile games, representing 27% of all father-infant games. In contrast to mothers, fathers more often engaged in limb movement games in which their behavior attempted to arouse the infant. These limb movement games (whether or not accompanied by verbal games) occurred in 31% of all father-infant sessions (36% of sessions in which any games occurred) and represented 21% of all father-infant games, while they occurred in only 7% of all mother-infant sessions and represented only 4% of mother-infant games. All of these differences were significant (t-test).[10] Mothers also played frequent limb movement games but they were a different category in which the infant assumed a conventional motoric role such as pat-a-cake, peek-a-boo, or waving. These conventional limb movement games occurred significantly more often with mothers than with fathers.

In order to determine how early fathers and mothers began to play different kinds of games with their infants, data from sessions with the youngest infants (ages 4, 6, 8, and 10 weeks) were analyzed separately and compared with the full sample. Even at this young age, fathers played games with their infants

Table 1

Categorization of Games

Category	Definition	Sample Description
Tactile	Parent stimulates surface of an infant body part	Father runs fingers of one hand up the baby's leg to his arm
Limb movement	Parent moves infant's limbs in space without a traditional motoric role; parent's purpose appears to be that of arousing the infant	Father holds infant's arms and shakes them
Conventional Limb Movement	Parent moves infant's limbs in space with a traditional motoric role assumed by the infant (peek-a-boo, waving bye bye)	Mother does pat-a-cake while clapping infant's hands
Visual	Parent provides distal stimulation by motor movements that may be visually observed by the infant; motor activity lacks a traditional role; parents purpose appears to be that of maintaining the visual attention of the infant	Mother wiggles the fingers of her hands, infant very attentive to fingers
Conventional Visual	Parent provides distal stimulation by motor movements that may be visually observed by the infant; parent demonstrates a traditional motor activity (visual demonstration of pat-a-cake or peek-a-boo, clapping, waving bye bye)	Mother claps her own hands saying pat-a-cake
Combination	Parent combines two or more of the above categories in one game	Father alternates between tapping the infant on the chin and shaking his arms
Pure Verbal	Parent uses repetitive vocalizations	Mother repeatedly imitates baby's coos

Modified from Crawley, et al.[7]

Table 2

Types of Games Played by Parent and Infant

	% of all Games		% of all Sessions		% Sessions any Games Occurred	
	Mother-Infant	Father-Infant	Mother-Infant	Father-Infant	Mother-Infant	Father-Infant
Tactile	26.0	27.0	37.0	31.4	48.7 *	36.1
Limb Movement	4.3 *	21.3	7.4 *	31.4	9.7 *	36.1
Conventional Limb Movement	8.6 *	2.2	14.8 *	3.7	19.5 *	4.2
Visual	35.8 *	20.2	46.2	31.4	60.9 *	36.1
Conventional Visual	2.1	3.3	3.7	1.8	4.8	2.1
Combination	8.6	5.6	9.2	7.4	12.2	8.5
Pure Verbal	14.1	20.2	22.2	29.6	29.2	34.0

*p ≤ 0.05 (t test)[10]

during 92% of their sessions while mothers and infants played games during 87% of their sessions. Furthermore, differences between games played with mothers and fathers were almost identical to those seen for the full sample: fathers played significantly more limb movement games with their infants than did mothers. Other differences while similar in direction to the full sample were not significant because of the small sample size. These games were seen with infants as young as 23 days of age. As infants grew older, the games were repeated and expanded. For example, in one family when the infant was one month of age, the father repeatedly tapped his infant, circling her mouth with his finger. He repeated this game several times while repeatedly verbalizing "Come on." The infant responded by alerting, stilling, opening her mouth, and vocalizing "Ahh," softly. By three months of age, the games had expanded to incorporate limb movement games and conventional motor activities such as clapping and "pat-a-cake," along with verbal accentuation ("ahh boo," "Come on," and clicking noises). These games were seen with both male and female infants, although the sample size was too small to assess the impact of the infant's sex on the kinds of games played.

DISCUSSION

Both parents played almost one game per minute with their infants, aged one to six months, during a laboratory play observation. The visual games more often played by mothers may represent a more distal attention-maintaining form of interactive play than the more proximal, idiosyncratic limb movement games played more often by fathers. Stern[6] has suggested that the goal of most mother-infant games is to facilitate an optimal level of arousal in the infant in order to foster attention to social signals. The more proximal games of infants and fathers may serve to modulate the infant's attention and arousal in a more accentuated fashion than occurs during the more distal games of infants and mothers.

It has previously been suggested that accentuated shifts in the temporal quality of stimulation may increase the infant's arousal.[11] While the data presented here suggest that mothers and fathers differ in the behaviors they use to engage their infants in games, further attention to the temporal qualities of these games, their repetition and pause patterns, may provide additional evidence of differences between mother- and father-infant interaction.

While the results of this study are based on a small, white, middle class sample studied in a laboratory, the findings are consistent with descriptions of parental play with older infants both at home and in a laboratory. Studies by Power and Parke of the games played with eight-month-old infants in a lab showed that mothers played more distal games while fathers engaged in more physical games.[12] In another study by Lamb, fathers more often picked up their infants to play idiosyncratic, rough-and-tumble, physical games, whereas mother were more likely to play with toys or use conventional games such as peek-a-boo.[3] By age 2½, Clarke-Stewart reported that when parents were asked to engage the child in specific play activities at home, fathers were better able to engage the child in play. Father's play with his child was more likely to be proximal (as was described for younger infants), social, physical, arousing, and briefer in duration, and fathers reported that they enjoyed it more than mothers.[8, 13] Infants at eight months responded more positively to play with fathers than mothers,[3] and by 2½ years of age not only preferred to play with fathers but were judged to be more involved and excited with them.[8]

The data from the present study suggest that interactive games with parents even during the first 6 months of infancy provide differentiated experiences for the infant. One can speculate about the developmental significance of these games. Visual games and conventional limb movement games, more common with mothers, may allow the establishment and consolidation of rules of interchange which are both basic social skills and facilitate later language development. Limb movement games which appear more arousing for the infant and which are more common with fathers may encourage the infant's interest in novel stimuli and facilitate alternate forms of social play.

REFERENCES

1. Parke R, Sawin D: Infant characteristics and behavior as elicitors of maternal and paternal responsibility in the newborn period. Paper presented to Society for Research in Child Development, Denver, 1973.
2. Parke R: Perspectives on father-infant interaction. In J D Osofsky (Ed.), *Handbook of Infancy.* New York, John Wiley, 1979.
3. Lamb M E: Fathers: Forgotten contributors to child development. *Human Dev 18:*245-266, 1975.
4. Lamb M E: The development of mother-infant and father-infant attachments in the second year of life. *Dev Psych, 13:*637-648, 1977.
5. Bruner J, Jolly A and Sylva K (Eds.): *Play.* New York, Basic Books, 1976.
6. Stern D N: The goal and structure of mother-infant play. *J Acad Child Psychiat 13:*402-421, 1974.
7. Crawley S, Rogers P, Friedman S, Iacobbo M, Criticos A, Richardson L and Thompson M: Developmental changes in the structure of mother-infant play. *Dev Psych 14:*30-36, 1978.
8. Clarke-Stewart K A: And daddy makes three: The father's impact on mother and child. *Child Dev 49:*466-478, 1978.
9. Brazelton T B, Tronick E, Adamson L, Als H and Wise S: Early mother-infant reciprocity. In R Hinde . (Ed.), *Parent-Infant Interaction.* Ciba Foundation Symposium No. 33. Amsterdam, Elsevier, 1975.
10. Bruning J L and Kintz B L: *Computational Handbook of Statistics.* Glenview, Scott, Foresman, 1968.
11. Stern, D N: Temporal expectancies of social behaviors in mother-infant play. In E Thoman (Ed.), *The Origins of the Infant's Responsiveness.* New York, Erlbaum, 1977.
12. Power T B, Parke R D: Toward a taxonomy of father-infant and mother-infant play patterns. Paper presented to the Society for Research in Child Development, San Francisco, 1979.
13. Clarke-Stewart K A: The father's contribution to children's cognitive and social development in early childhood. In F A Pedersen (Ed.), *The Father-Infant Relationship: Observational Studies in a Family Setting.* New York, Holt, Rinehart, and Winston, 1980.

Infant Mental Health Journal, Vol. 2, No. 4, Winter 1981

Fathers' Interactions with Their High-Risk Infants

Tiffany Field, PhD

ABSTRACT: Fathers' face-to-face interactions with their 4-month-old high-risk infants were compared to mothers' interactions with the same infants and to those interactions of fathers and mothers of normal infants. The high-risk infants were less attentive and less affectively responsive than normal infants, and their mothers were more active. Fathers of both high-risk and normal infants engaged in more game playing and laughed more frequently than mothers during interactions. Although the behaviors of the normal and high-risk infants differed, as did the behaviors of mothers interacting with them, the fathers engaged in similar amounts of activity, smiling, laughing and playing games with normal and high-risk infants. Fathers may be less disturbed than mothers by their high-risk infants' lesser responsivity.

Dozens of studies on the early interactions of high-risk infants and their mothers appear in journals and in separate volumes on the subject.[1,2] However, there are very few studies on the early interactions of high-risk infants and their fathers.[3-5] Although several researchers have suggested that fathers may indirectly affect the early interactions of their high-risk infants via the support they provide the infants' mothers,[6,8] little attention has been paid to the way fathers themselves interact with their high-risk infants. The literature on normal infant-father interactions suggests that fathers are more "playful"[9-11] and engage in infant games with their infants more frequently than mothers.[3] Because early game playing may provide a foundation for learning interaction turn-taking skills, fathers may play an important role in the developing interaction skills of their high-risk infants.

The literature on interactions of high-risk infants and their mothers generally depicts the high-risk infant as less attentive, less expressive, less

Tiffany Field is affiliated with the Mailman Center for Child Development at the University of Miami Medical School. Reprint requests should be addressed to Dr. Field at P.O. Box 016820, Miami, FL 33101.

The author would like to thank the parents and infants who participated in this study. Further thanks go to George Ting who assisted with data collection. This research was partially supported by grants from the National Foundation/March of Dimes and from the Massachusetts Public Health Department.

0613-9641/81/1500-0249$00.95

responsive, more irritable and generally more difficult than normal infants. Several groups of high-risk infants, including preterm infants,[12] preterm infants with respiratory distress syndrome,[13,15] post-term infants with postmaturity syndrome.[14] Down's syndrome infants,[16] blind,[17] and autistic-like infants,[18-20] have been similarly described. Their mothers frequently are overstimulating, controlling, intrusive and less sensitive to the signals of their infants. In general, mothers of high-risk infants seem to "try too hard" to engage their infants and these attempts often appear counterproductive inasmuch as their infants frequently respond with more gaze aversion and irritability. Generalizations of this kind, of course, are tempered by the considerable individual variability that occurs both between and within these groups, but high-risk infants and their mothers, in general, seem "to have less fun."

Fathers of normal infants are notable for their playful, funloving approach to early interactions. They typically engage in game playing and physical activity more frequently than mothers.[3,10,11] These characteristics are generally reported except for fathers who are primary caregivers or those who take care of the infant during the daytime.[3] Those fathers are more similar to mothers than to secondary caregiver fathers. They engage in less game playing and tactile/kinesthetic stimulation and show more of the behaviors characteristic of mothers, for example, smiling, high-pitched vocalizations and imitative behaviors.

A question of interest to us was whether fathers of high-risk infants might behave like fathers of normal infants or like mothers of high-risk infants. Some of the interpretations proposed for the overactive, over-controlling behavior of mothers during interactions with their high-risk infants include the mothers' disappointment and depression related to having a fragile, difficult baby instead of a "Gerber" baby. Fathers may not be as vulnerable to this feeling of having failed to produce a normal, health baby, and thus they may relate in similar ways to normal and high-risk infatns. Another interpretation of the mothers' differential behavior with high-risk infants relates to the infant being an unresponsive interaction partner for which the mother attempts to compensate. Fathers might be expected to behave differently toward high-risk infants for the same reasons, particularly if they become more involved in caregiving of the more difficult-to-care-for-high-risk infant, may be less aware of the infant's lack of responsivity or may be aware that the infant is difficult or less responsive but are less affected by this. Since the reasons for the mothers' atypical interactive behaviors with high-risk infants are yet very uncertain, any hypotheses regarding the fathers' behavior are tenuous at best.

The present study compared the behaviors of mothers and fathers of normal and high-risk infants during their early face-to-face interactions. The high-risk infants of this study were preterm infants who had experienced the respiratory distress syndrome. Several attentive and affective behaviors of the infants and their parents were coded in an attempt to characterize their early interactions.

METHOD

Sample

The sample was comprised of 24 normal and 24 high-risk infants and their parents. The normal infants were full term and healthy and the high-risk infants were pre-term infants (mean gestational age = 32 weeks; mean birthweight = 1800 grams), who experienced respiratory distress syndrome and averaged 32 days in the intensive care nursery at the neonatal stage. All infants were later-born children of middle socioeconomic status, white parents who averaged 25 years of age (range = 24-28 years).

Procedure

The infants and parents visited our interaction laboratory when the infants were 4 months post expected date of delivery, an age adjustment to control for any maturational age differences posed by the varying gestational ages of the preterm infants.

The interaction session commenced with a warm-up feeding period during which the infants and parents could become acclimated to the video lab and to ensure that the infants were in a similar state, a post-feeding state. Following the feeding, the infant was positioned in an upright infant seat on a table situated in a curtained alcove. The surrounding curtains were used to diminish any distractions created by the video lab equipment in the simulated living-room furnishings of the lab. The mother or father was seated opposite the infant in an *en face* position approximately 18 inches from the infant. Two video cameras were positioned 6 feet from the dyad and were partially hidden by the surrounding curtains. The use of two cameras and a split screen generator enabled a viewing of both the parent's and infant's faces, one on each side of the video screen.

Three-minute face-to-face interactions were then videotaped for each of the infant-mother and infant-father dyads. The order of mother and father interactions was counterbalanced across subjects to control for any order effects of interacting first with mother or father. Both mothers and fathers were simply asked to pretend that they were at home at their kitchen table playing with their infant. A one-minute interval separated the infant's interactions with mother and father.

Coding

Videotapes of the face-to-face interactions were coded by trained observers naive to the purposes of the study. Coding was done via 20-key Esterline-Angus event recorders by two observers simultaneously viewing the videotapes. The output of the event recorder provided us a record of the frequency and absolute duration of the behaviors coded.

The behaviors coded and their interobserver reliabilities (number of coder agreements divided by the sum of agreements and disagreements) were as follows: 1) parent behaviors included: (a) amount of activity including vocalizations (.93) and discrete tactile stimulation (.84)(e.g. poking and moving infant's limbs); (b) smiling (.91); (c) laughing (.97); and (d) game-playing of any recognized infant game such as pat-a-cake, peek-a-boo, I'm gonna get you, tell-me-a-story, so big, etc. (.92);[23] 2. Infant behaviors included: (a) gaze aversion (.91); (b) smiling (.87); (c) grimacing (.83); (d) positive vocalizations—cooing, girgling (.83); and (e) negative vocalizations—fussing, crying (.83).[3]

In addition, the mothers and fathers were asked to complete the Infant Temperament Questionnaire.[24]

RESULTS

The data were analyzed by a 2 (condition of infant-term or preterm) × 2 (parent—mother or father) multivariate analysis of variance.[25] Because this analysis yielded significant values for both condition of infant and parent factors, univariate analyses of variance were performed for each of the variables. Significant interaction effects were examined by Bonferroni t tests.[26]

Main effects for condition of the infant were as follows: Parents of pre-term infants versus parents of term infants were: (1) more active or provided more verbal and tactile stimulation, $F(1,45) = 8.07$, $p < .01$ (see Figure 1); and (2) engaged in less gameplaying, $F(1,45) = 5.11$, $p < .05$ (see Table 1). Pre-term infants, as compared to term infants (1) gaze averted more frequently, $F(1,45) = 13.08$, $p < .001$; (2) smiled less frequently, $F(1,45) = 9.17$, $p < .005$; (3) grimaced more frequently, $F(1,45) = 5.32$, $p < .05$; (4) uttered fewer positive vocalizations, $F(1,45) = 10.16$, $p < .005$; and (5) fussed and cried more frequently, $F(1,45) = 12.94$, $p < .001$.

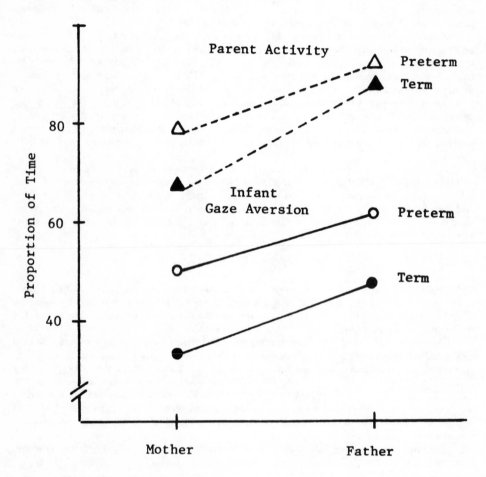

Main effects for the parent factor were as follows: Fathers (1) were more active, $F(1,45) = 8.21$, $p < .01$, (see Figure 1); (2) laughed more frequently, $F(1,45) = 11.42$, $p < .005$, (see Table 1); (3) engaged in more game playing, $F(1,45) = 7.61$, $p < .01$, and a greater number of different games $F(1,45) = 6.14$, $p < .05$. Infants in the presence of fathers: (1) gaze averted a greater proportion of the interaction time, $F(1,45) = 6.09$, $p < .05$; (2) smiled more

Table 1. Mean frequency of behaviors or mean proportion of interaction time behaviors were observed for term and preterm infants and their parents.

	Father		Mother	
Parent				
Behavior	Term	Preterm	Term	Preterm
% Smiling	29	24	33	17
% Laughing	13	11	8	2
% Gameplaying	44	35	38	19
# Different Games	5.9	4.1	4.8	1.6
Infant				
Behavior				
# Smiles	10.1	7.3	8.2	3.4
# Grimaces	1.4	2.2	2.4	4.1
# Positive Vocalizations	8.1	4.8	5.2	2.3
# Negative Vocalizations	.4	5.0	.3	3.2

frequently, $F(1,45) = 8.02$, $p < .01$; and (3) uttered more positive vocalizations, $F(1,45) = 4.81$, $p < .05$.

There were parent by condition of infant interaction effects for parent smiling ($F(1,45) = 9.13$, $p < .005$, laughing ($F(1,45) = 8.76$, $p < .01$), game playing ($F(1,45) = 9.71$, $p < .005$). Interaction effects for infant behaviors included smiling ($F(1,45) = 6.21$, $p < .05$), grimaces ($F(1,45) = 5.17$, $p < .05$) and positive vocalizations ($F(1,45) = 7.42$, $p < .01$).

Post hoc comparisons of these interaction effects yielded significant t values at least at the .05 level of significance which suggested the following: mothers of pre-term infants showed the least amount of smiling, laughing, game playing and number of different games. Pre-term infants in the presence of their mothers showed the least amount of smiling and positive vocalizations and the greatest number of grimaces. While the mothers of term and pre-term infants differed on every coded behavior at a significance level of at least $p < .05$, differences between fathers of term and preterm infants failed to reach this level of significance.

Mean ratings of infant temperament were as follows: 1) pre-term infants averaged 3.8 (on a 4 point scale) as rated by mothers and 3.8 as rated by fathers; 2) term infants averaged 2.2 as rated by mothers and 2.3 as rated by fathers. Although a main effect for infant condition suggested that parents of preterm infants rated their infant's temperament as being more difficult than was suggested by ratings of term infants by their parents ($F(1,45) = 12.01, p <$ .005), there were no main effects for the parent factor or parent by infant condition interaction effects.

DISCUSSION

That pre-term infants were less attentive or gaze averted more frequently, showed less frequent positive facial and vocal expressions and more frequent negative facial and vocal expressions is not surprising in light of previous reports on the interactive behaviors of pre-term infants,[12] and particularly pre-term infants who experienced respiratory distress syndrome.[13-15] The greater amounts of activity observed for the mothers of pre-term infants are also consistent with previous reports.[13-15]

Although it is not clear why mothers are more active with their high-risk infants, a number of potential explanations have been offered. Because their high-risk infants are generally less attentive and less responsive, mothers may assume that they need to provide more verbal and tactile stimulation to elicit a response. Frustration from not eliciting responses may lead to further activity. Chapple[21] demonstrated that an adult subject will become more verbal in the presence of a silent, relatively unresponsive experimenter. An adult subject, faced with an active experimenter will become less active. The parent of the high-risk infant may become more active for similar reasons, due to a preference for active interaction or the discomfort associated with silence. And the infant, like the adult with the active experimenter, may become increasingly less responsive, less attentive and more irritable.

The pre-term RDS infant may have a higher threshold to stimulation, but a narrower range of information processing and arousal modulation abilities.[22] The parents of these infants may have to provide more stimulation to elicit an attentive response, but then more carefully modulate their stimulation so as not to exceed the lesser developed processing and arousal modulation abilities of their infants. The lesser incidence of game playing in the pre-term infant-parent dyads may also relate to the infants' lesser responsivity. Game playing involves turn-taking and reciprocal responsivity. When infants smile and laugh in response to parents' games, the parents will often persist or slightly modify the game.[23] Without the affective response of the infant, parents often cease playing the game.

The greater frequency of gameplaying and laughing on the part of the fathers is also consistent with previous reports.[3, 11] Although it is not clear why fathers play games more frequently, some have suggested that they may not view young infants as being as fragile as mothers view them. They may expect less of the infant as conversationalist and consider that the infant's skills are yet limited to looking, smiling and being a participant observer, ready to be entertained. Infants may show more positive affect and more gaze aversion in the presence of their fathers because of the arousing nature of the games their fathers more frequently play.

Fathers of pre-term infants were somewhat more active (talking and touching) than fathers of term infants and smiled, laughed, and played games less frequently. Howerver, the differences between the behaviors of fathers with pre-term and term infants were not significant as they were for the comparisons between behaviors of mothers of pre-term and term infants. In the absence of attitudinal data of the parents, we can only speculate about these differences. Fathers seemed aware that there were differences in the attentiveness and responsivity of their infants, as manifested by their rating their infants difficult on the Carey Temperament Scale. However, they did not appear as disturbed as the mothers by their infants' lesser attentiveness or responsivity. Their positive affect, smiling and laughing, occurred more frequently than that of the mothers of high-risk infants, suggesting that they may be less frustrated by their infants' lesser responsiveness. Fathers may require less reinforcement or responsivity for the games they play, and view their role more as entertainer of the very young infant and less as conversation partner. Another possibility which cannot be addressed by these data is that mothers and fathers may be affected differently by the videotaping situation or by their perceptions of the experimenter's expectations for this situation.

This study suggests, then, that the interactions of high-risk infants and their fathers may be less disturbed than those of the infants and their mothers, although, the reasons for fathers behaving similarly with normal and high-risk infants are not clear. A comparison of the parents' awareness of the developmental course of these infants, their feelings and attitudes about the infants' interaction behavior and their own role during the interactions, and their expectations for their infants' developing social skills may reveal some of the reasons for fathers treating their high-risk infants very much like normal infants but very differently than the way mothers relate to the same infants.

REFERENCES

1. Field T, Sostek A, Goldberg S, Shuman H: *Infants Born at Risk.* New York, Spectrum Publications, 1979.
2. Field T, Goldberg S, Stern D, Sostek A, (Eds): *High-risk Infants and Children: Adult and Peer Interactions.* New York, Academic Press, 1980.
3. Field T: Interaction behaviors of primary versus secondary caretaker fathers. *Dev Psych 14:* 183-184, 1978.
4. Field, T: Gaze behavior of normal and high-risk infants during early interactions. *J Am Acad Child Psychiat, 20:*308-317 1981.
5. Parke R D, Hymel S, Power T G, Tinsley BR: Fathers and risk: A hospital-based model of intervention. In D B Sawin, R C Hawkins, L O Walker and J H Penticuff (Eds), *Exceptional Infant: Psychosocial Risks in Infant Environment Transactions.* (Vol 4) New York, Brunner/Mazel, 1980.
6. Herzog J M: Disturbances in parenting high-risk infants: Clinical impressions and hypotheses. In T Field, A Sostek, S Goldberg and H H Shuman (Eds), *Infants Born at Risk.* New York, Spectrum Publications, 1980.

7. Klaus M H, Kennell J H: *Maternal Infant Bonding.* St. Louis, C. V. Mosby Co., 1976.
8. Minde K, Trehub S, Corter C, Boukydis C, Celhoffer B, Martin P: Mother-child relationships in the premature nursery: An observational study. Unpublished manuscript, Department of Psychiatry, The Hospital for Sick Children, Toronto, Canada, 1977.
9. Lamb M E: Father-infant and mother-infant interaction in the first year of life. *Child Dev 48:*167-181, 1977.
10. Parke R D: Perspectives on father-infant interaction. In J D Osofsky (Ed), *Handbook of Infant Development.* New York, Wiley & Sons, 1979.
11. Yogman M W, Dixon S, Tronick E, Adamson L, Als A, Brazelton T B: Development of infant social interaction with fathers. Paper presented at EPA, New York, April 1976.
12. Brown J V, Bakeman R: Relationships of human mothers with their infants during the first year of life: Effect of prematurity. In R W Bell and W P Smotherman (Eds), *Maternal Influences and Early Behavior.* New York, Spectrum, 1979.
13. DiVitto B, Goldberg S: The effects of newborn medical status on early parent-infant interaction. In T Field, A Sostek, S Goldberg and H H Shuman (Eds), *Infants Born at Risk.* New York, Spectrum, 1979.
14. Field T: Effects of early separation, interactive deficits and experimental manipulations on infant-mother face-to-face interaction. *Child Dev 48:*763-771, 1977.
15. Field T: Interaction patterns of high-risk and normal infants. In T Field, A Sostek, S Goldberg and H H Shuman (Eds), *Infants Born at Risk.* New York, Spectrum Publications, 1979.
16. Jones O: Mother-child communication in very young Down's syndrome and normal children. In T Field et al (Eds), *High-risk Infants and Children: Adult and Peer Interactions.* New York, Academic Press, 1980.
17. Als H, Tronick E, Brazelton T B: Stages of early behavioral organization: The study of a sighted infant and a blind infant in interaction with their mothers. In T Field, S Goldberg, D Stern and A M Sostek (Eds), *High-risk Infants and Children: Adult and Peer Interactions.* New York, Academic Press, 1980.
18. Kubicek L: Mother interactions of twins: An autistic and non-autistic twin. In T Field, S Goldberg, D Stern and A M Sostek (Eds), *High-risk Infants and Children: Adult and Peer Interactions.* New York, Academic Press, 1980.
19. Massie H N: Pathologic interactions in infancy. In T Field et al. (Eds), *High-risk Infants and Children: Adult and Peer Interactions.* New York, Academic Press, 1980.
20. Stern D: A micro-analysis of mother-infant interaction: Behavior reulating social contact between a mother and her 3½-month-old twins. *J Am Acad Child Psychiat 10:*501-517, 1972.
21. Chapple E D: Experimental production of transients in human interaction. *Nature 228:*630-633, 1970.
22. Field T: Infant arousal, attention and affect during early interactions. In L Lipsitt and K K Rovee-Collier (Eds), *Advances in Infant Development* (Vol. 1), Hillsdale, New Jersey, Lawrence Erlbaum Associates, 1981.
23. Field T: Games parents play with normal and high-risk infants. *Child Psychiat Hum Dev 10:*41-48, 1979.
24. Carey W B: A simplified method for measuring infant temperament. *J Pediatrics 77:*188-194, 1970.
25. Myers J L: *Fundamentals of Experimental Design,* Boston, Allyn & Bacon, 1972.
26. Morrison D F: *Multivariate Statistical Methods.* New York, McGraw Hill, 1967.

Infant Mental Health Journal, Vol. 2, No. 4, Winter 1981

Cesarean Childbirth: Psychological Implications for Mothers and Fathers

Frank A. Pedersen, PhD
Martha J. Zaslow, PhD
Richard L. Cain, MA
Barbara J. Anderson, PhD

ABSTRACT: Home observations, ratings of interaction, and interviews were carried out in families with first-born 5-month-old infants. Comparisons were made between two groups of families differing as to whether the childbirth had been a Cesarean or vaginal delivery. Fathers whose babies had been born by Cesarean delivery reported greater involvement in child care and were rated as more responsive to infant distress. Both mothers and fathers tended to show less animation in interactions with their infants following a Cesarean delivery: mothers engaged less frequently in vigorous physical stimulation and showed less reciprocal positive affect with their infants, and fathers smiled less at their infants.

Cesarean delivery rates have tripled in the United States in the last decade.[1] With the sharp increase in Cesarean childbirth there has been growing concern that this medical procedure may have important psychological consequences. Those who have had direct contact with women during and after the childbirth process, especially childbirth educators and nurses, have reported that they observe a variety of problems: fear and stress in laboring women who have to adjust to an imminent surgical procedure when a Cesarean delivery was unanticipated; feelings of guilt, failure, and anger in mothers who prepared for a low medication vaginal delivery; separations of mothers and infants rather than the expected immediate contact after birth; difficulty in first feeding and caregiving attempts by mothers who are groggy, in pain, or unable to hold their newborns; and difficulties upon returning home from the hospital for mothers who must assume the demands of infant care at a time when they themselves have unusual needs for physical and emotional recovery.

The authors are affiliated with Child and Family Research Branch of the National Institute of Child Health and Human Development, Bethesda, MD. A version of this paper was presented at the International Conference on Infant Studies, New Haven, CT, April 1980. The authors thank Leon Yarrow for constructive criticism of the manuscript, Nancy Gist for assistance in the investigation, and Barbara Wright for preparation of the manuscript.

0613-9641/81/1500-0257$00.95   *257*

A limited body of research is beginning to corroborate these observations. Studies by Entwisle,[2] Marut and Mercer,[3] and Bradley[4] have found that Cesarean mothers have significantly less positive perceptions of the birth. Marut and Mercer report that a majority of women in their sample described a Cesarean delivery as "a shock," "a big disappointment," or "totally different from what I expected." More depressive affect has been found in these mothers in the postpartum period,[4] at 1 month,[5] (a near significant difference), and at 2 months.[2] Lipson and Tilden[6] report that psychological assimilation and acceptance of a childbirth "is often longer and more difficult for Cesarean mothers than for women who deliver vaginally....Although some women assimilate the experience almost as rapidly as in vaginal birth, for others the process is drawn out over years and may require psychotherapeutic intervention" (p.607).

The growing awareness of the psychological impact of Cesarean delivery on mothers has not, however, been accompanied by parallel consideration of possible effects of this birth experience on fathers. On the one hand, the limited concern with fathers' reactions to Cesarean birth is understandable: it is the women who must go through the surgery and recover from it. On the other hand, the lack of research into the impact on fathers of Cesarean delivery contrasts with widespread recognition of the father's experiences when present during a vaginal delivery, and the importance of his presence for his partner.[7,8]

There is good reason to suspect that fathers as well as mothers have a distinctly different set of experiences when their children are born by Cesarean as opposed to vaginal delivery. Men too may experience disappointment that the delivery did not go as planned, and may blame themselves for this outcome. A father who is present at a Cesarean delivery may have a sense of participation in his infant's birth, but simultaneously has to cope with the psychological impact of surgery being performed on a loved one. If a father is asked to leave while a Cesarean delivery is performed, there may be acute disappointment that he was not able to participate in the birth or have a supportive relationship with the mother. Whether or not a father is present during the delivery, he may experience heightened fear for both his wife and child, given the emergency medical procedures, and the fact that the infant may be observed in a special care nursery. Finally, the needs of the mother during the long period of post-operative recovery may indirectly have an influence on the developing father-child relationship.

In this article we will present evidence from an exploratory study that Cesarean delivery of a first born infant is an event that has implications for both fathers and mothers, and further that the impact of such a delivery on the family endures at least through the infant's fifth month.

METHOD

Sample

In a sample of 41 non-minority, two-parent families with a first-born infant, there were 6 Cesarean deliveries (a 15% rate); the balance had normal vaginal deliveries. The sample was recruited from the Washington, D.C. area in 1976 through childbirth preparation groups which encouraged low medication deliveries with the father present. As is characteristic of families who select such preparation experience, parents tended to be well educated (college level) and they had deferred childbearing for several years. The mean age for the mothers in the sample was 29 and for the fathers 31. The parents had been married a mean of 4.6 years. At age 5 months, the period when our assessments took place, all infants were reported to be healthy and developing normally.

Although *mean* scores on all background variables were not significantly different for the two groups of families, the larger group that had vaginal deliveries had a much greater *range* on background measures. Therefore, of the 35 families that had vaginal deliveries, cases were chosen that were most similar to the Cesarean families on the basis of parental age, education, and years of marriage. Seventeen families were selected for a comparison group.

Procedure

Participating families were visited four times in their homes when their infants were 5 months old. An initial visit was made to obtain informed constent, answer questions, interview the parents regarding the pregnancy and delivery experience, obtain background demographic information, and ask about the family's current caregiving practices. Subsequently two one-hour observations were conducted when both parents were home, typically during the early evening, and there was a 90-minute observation of mother and infant when the father was not home. Following each observation, the observer made ratings of some qualitative aspects of parent-infant, and spouse interactions. Ratings were made on 5 point scales for such measures as the extent of reciprocal positive affect expressed between parent and infant, and the extent to which the parents shared pleasure in their baby's behavior.

A time-sampling procedure was followed for the observations, with 10 second observation periods followed by 20 second recording periods, continuing throughout each session. Selected behaviors were recorded from the interactions of all possible dyads in the 3-person family: mother and infant, father and infant, and mother and father. Behavior categories were not mutually exclusive, and all behaviors that occurred were recorded. Parent behavior with the infant fell into 4 categories: (1) distance receptor interaction (mutual visual regard, verbalization to the baby, vocalization to the baby, and smiles); (2) near receptor interaction (holding, rocking, vigorous tactile/kinesthetic stimulation, and touching); (3) play (social play, and directing the infant's attention to objects); and (4) caregiving (feeding liquids, feeding solids, washing or cleaning, and dressing or diapering the infant). Infant behaviors recorded included the baby's looking at the mother's or the father's face, positive vocalization, smiling, fussing or crying, resisting a parental behavior, and exploratory behavior. Spouse interaction behaviors included talking about the baby, talking about something or someone other than the baby, exchanging positive affect, exchanging negative affect, giving instrumental assistance to the spouse, and making a request of the spouse. Detailed descriptions of each behavior and of the observation system are available on request.[9]

The data were collected by 3 observers who shared in the method development and observed 10 cases prior to and during the data collection period for reliability purposes. Reliability for behaviors, computed using product-moment correlations on frequency scores for each behavior for pairs of observers, ranged from .70 to .99. The observers were blind to hypotheses concerning the effects of Cesarean childbirth.

Analysis

Analysis consisted of comparing with *t*-tests the data from interviews, observations, and ratings for families where there had been a Cesarean childbirth with those where there had been a vaginal delivery. The *t*-test program from the Statistical Package for the Social Science,[10] which was used for these comparisions, provides values for *t* based on pooled as well as separate sample variance estimates. The *t* values, appropriate degrees of freedom and *p* values will be reported according to whether group variances differed or could be pooled. Considering the total number of comparisons made and the size of the sample, the findings are viewed as exploratory. It is hoped that hypotheses will be generated that may be confirmed in future investigations.

RESULTS

Descriptive information from the interview about childbirth circumstances identified several ways in which Cesarean and vaginal deliveries differed in this sample. Four of the six Cesarean deliveries involved a general anesthesia, while none of the vaginal deliveries did. None of the fathers were present for the Cesarean deliveries, whereas when there was a vaginal delivery, over 80% of the fathers were present during both labor and delivery. The mother's stay in the hospital was significantly longer after a Cesarean delivery (7 days as opposed to 3.35 days, $t(21) = 7.20$, $p < .0001$). After Cesarean birth, mothers had to overcome more severe disruptions in adapting to their infants (e.g. difficulty in feeding, separations of mother and infant due to infection; $t(21) = 2.38$, $p < .05$). We note that some of these findings are characteristic of hospital practices for this cohort. Physicians now show much greater willingness to perform a Cesarean delivery with a regional anesthetic and with the father present.

On the basis of the 5-month observations, the qualitative ratings of family interaction, and the parental interviews, there were relatively few instances of differences in maternal behavior related to birth experience. Only two differences were statistically significant. In the evening observations, mothers who had experienced Cesarean childbirth engaged in significantly fewer instances of vigorous tactile and kinesthetic stimulation of the infant ($t(19) = 2.39$, $p < .05$). There were four observational measures of physical handling of the infant; each was numerically lower for the Cesarean mothers, though only the frequency of vigorous physical stimulation was statistically significant. The second finding was that the mother-infant interaction in the Cesarean group showed significantly less reciprocal positive affect ($t(21) = 2.22$, p. $< .05$). This was based on the observers' ratings made during the daytime period when the father was not at home. The two measures together, vigorous physical handling and reciprocal positive affect, imply that mothers of Cesarean delivered infants interacted in a less spirited way than in the comparison group.

A pattern of differences in father-infant interaction related to birth experience appeared to be one in which the fathers of Cesarean delivered infants showed greater concern for the baby's care and physical well-being. On the basis of interview data, fathers of Cesarean infants reported engaging in significantly more caregiving ($t(21) = 2.98$, $p < .01$). That is, during periods when both parents were together with the infant, fathers of Cesarean delivered infants were more likely to share caregiving responsibilities in several different areas on an equal basis with the mother. In contrast, fathers in the normal comparison group tended to "help out," with the mothers still meeting the major proportion of caregiving needs. A similar pattern was found in the observations, though differences were not statistically significant. Three out of four time-sampled caregiving measures were numerically higher for fathers of Cesarean delivered infants.

Fathers of Cesarean delivered infants were also rated by the observers as significantly more responsive to the infant's crying and fussing than were the fathers in the comparison group (t(21) = 3.6, p<.01). Though not statistically significant, there was a suggestion that the *pattern* of parental responsiveness was reversed, depending upon birth circumstances: fathers of Cesarean delivered infants appeared more responsive to the infant's crying and fussing than did their wives, while fathers of vaginally delivered infants were rated as less responsive than their wives.

In spite of fathers of Cesarean-delivered infants showing greater caregiving involvement and responsiveness to distress, there is no indication that they engaged in increased rates of purely social interaction. In the 3-person situation, 9 of 10 time-sampled measures of social interaction (non-caregiving behaviors) were numerically *lower* for the fathers of Cesarean delivered infants compared to the fathers of vaginally delivered infants. All measures fit this pattern except rocking and cuddling the infant, which often is associated with responding to distress cues. Across the total observation time fathers of Cesarean delivered infants smiled significantly less than the comparison fathers (t(17) = 2.28, p <.05), and these infants, in turn, smiled significantly less toward their fathers than the infants did in the comparison group (t(21) = 2.06, p = .05).

DISCUSSION

To summarize, after a Cesarean childbirth, fathers of 5-month-old infants reported greater participation in child care tasks than other fathers, and were observed to be more responsive to infant distress. Mothers who had Cesarean deliveries engaged in less vigorous physical stimulation of their infants, and when alone with them in the daytime were rated as showing less reciprocal positive affect in interaction with their infants. Fathers whose babies had been born by Cesarean delivery smiled less at their infants, and their infants smiled less at them.

Given the small sample size and the post hoc nature of the analyses, these results are best viewed as exploratory, and as we have noted, as sources of hypotheses for future research. Our findings suggest two specific hypotheses: (1) after a Cesarean birth there is a heightening of paternal involvement in caring for the physical needs of the infant, yet (2) some diminution for both parents in the expression of positive affect towards the infant.

It is plausible that the pattern of interaction within the family described by these hypotheses would have its roots in differing postpartum experiences for parents following Cesarean and vaginal deliveries. Our findings and the findings of other researchers suggest that following a Cesarean childbirth mothers must face three sources of difficulty in assuming the maternal role: (1) physical discomfort and exhaustion in the aftermath of major surgery; (2) the need to recover emotionally from surgery for which there was little preparation, and indeed which may have gone counter to an expectation of minimal medical intervention in childbirth; and (3) delays and disruptions in mother-infant contact after the birth. Marut and Mercer[11] found that after a Cesarean delivery mothers felt they had "little physical or emotional energy for mothering" (p. 11), and perhaps reflecting this state, they also found that these mothers were significantly more hesitant to name their infants than other mothers.

If the initial adaptation period with the infant is unusually taxing for the Cesarean mother, it is likely that she needs additional support and assistance. Our data indicate that in many families it is the father who is called upon to provide supplemental caregiving, and that these fathers, in turn, appear to develop heightened sensitivity to distress cues emitted by the infant. If fathers develop greater involvement and competence in caregiving in the first few weeks after the infant's birth, motivated especially by the mother's needs in this period, this pattern may continue at least for several months. This interpretation is consistent with a study carried out in Sweden (Lind, 1974 as cited by Parke[12]) which indicates that "fathers who were provided the opportunity to learn and practice basic caregiving skills during the post-partum hospital period were more involved in the care of the infant and in household tasks at three months in the home" (p. 57).

It is also possible that it is the mother's needs for physical and emotional recovery in the first postpartum weeks that sets up a pattern of interaction in which she shows less positive affect and less frequent physically robust stimulation of the infant continuing through the fifth month. Alternately, the recovery process itself may continue through the fifth month and be manifested in the mother's less spirited behavior with her infant.

Our study suggests one clear interpretation of the tendency for fathers to exchange fewer smiles with their infants after a Cesarean delivery: as paternal behavior shifts towards caregiving activities it also shifts away from playful and purely social interaction, and thus away from a frequent context for the exchange of smiles. We know from previous research that social play is high on the hierarchy of behaviors fathers engage in with their infants while caregiving is low on the hierarchy.[12-14] Thus Cesarean delivery appears to selectively call forth behaviors for which fathers may have little preparation, expectancy or cultural support. Further research might address the question of whether greater participation in caregiving is experienced by fathers as pleasurable or burdensome.

An important implication of our findings is that Cesarean intervention programs should focus on both parents. It would be helpful to alert expectant parents to problems that characteristically· occur: that mothers should anticipate needing time to recover both physically and emotionally, and may find it difficult to engage in physical handling of the child in the postpartum period; and that fathers may anticipate greater caregiving responsibility. Research on other types of stress, including the stress involved in vaginal delivery, indicates that cognitive structuring of expectancies facilitates adaptation.[15] There is every reason to believe that such structuring would be helpful prior to Cesarean childbirth as well.

Our findings point to the need for longitudinal investigations of the impact of Cesarean delivery on the family. Specifically, research is needed to (1) confirm the pattern of family interaction found in this exploratory study; (2) examine how long differences endure; and (3) determine more precisely the psychological processes which underlie differences in family interaction that come about after differing childbirth experiences.

REFERENCES

1. Bottoms SF, Rosen MG, Sokol RJ: The increase in the Cesarean birth rate. *N Eng J Med 302:*559, 1980.
2. Entwisle DR: Cesarean section: Social and psychological factors. Proposal submitted to the National Institute of Child Health and Human Development, October, 1978.
3. Marut JS, Mercer RT: Comparison of primiparas' perceptions of vaginal and Cesarean births. *Nursing Res 28:*260, 1979.
4. Bradley CF: *The Effects of Hospital Experience on Postpartum Feelings and Attitudes of Women.* Unpublished doctoral dissertation. University of British Columbia, 1976.
5. Joy LA: *Ramifications of Cesarean Versus Vaginal Delivery for the Development of Maternal Attachment.* Read before the meeting of the Society for Research in Child Development, San Francisco, March, 1979.
6. Lipson JG, Tilden VP: Psychological integration of the cesarean birth experience. *Amer J Orthopsychiat 50:*598, 1980.
7. Greenberg M, Morris N: Engrossment: The newborn's impact upon the father. *Amer J Orthophsychiat 44:*520, 1974.
8. Henneborn WJ, Cogan R: The effect of husband participation on reported pain and probability of medication during labor and birth. *J Psychosomat Res 19:*215, 1975.
9. Pedersen F, Anderson B, Cain R: Family observation manual. Unpublished manuscript, 1975.
10. Nie NH, Hull CH, Jenkins JG, Steinbrenner K, Bent DH: *Statistical Package for the Social Sciences.* New York, McGraw-Hill, 1975.
11. Marut JS, Mercer RT: The Cesarean birth experience: implications for nursing. In D Affonso (Ed.), *Impact of Cesarean Birth.* Philadelphia, Davis, in press.
12. Parke RD: Perspectives on father-infant interaction. In JD Osofsky (Ed), *Handbook of Infant Development.* New York, Wiley, 1979.
13. Clarke-Stewart KA: And daddy makes three: the father's impact on mother and young child. *Child Dev 49:*466, 1978.
14. Lamb ME: Interaction between eight-month-old children and their fathers and mothers. In ME Lamb (Ed), *The Role of the Father in Child Development.* New York, Wiley, 1976.
15. Doering SG, Entwisle DR: Preparation during pregnancy and ability to cope with labor and delivery. *Amer J Orthopsychiat 45:*825, 1975.

Infant Mental Health Journal, Vol. 2, No. 4, Winter 1981

The Father Role:
An Update

Sharon Price-Bonham, PhD
Joe F. Pittman, Jr. MA
Charles O. Welch, III, PhD

In October, 1976 the senior author published "Bibliography of Literature Related to Roles of Fathers" in the *Family Coordinator* (Vol. 25, No. 3; Pp. 489-512).[1] At that time it was noted men were increasingly being encouraged to become more involved in parenthood. One of the goals of that publication was to bring the scattered literature in the area of fatherhood together. It included literature published 1964 through part of 1975. This present bibliography is another attempt toward this goal and includes father-related literature published 1975-1980.

Since the previous publication there appears to have been an increasing interest in research and other writings related to fathers. In addition, there have been some shifts in areas of interests. For example, the increase in the divorce/remarriage rate has been accompanied by a marked increase in literature related to divorced fathers, stepfathers, and single fathers. However, as before, there has been more interest in the absent father than the present father and much of the literature does not control for "degree of absence." For example, a father, even though divorced from a former spouse, could live in the same community or neighborhood and have very frequent contact with his children. In contrast, another father could have very infrequent or no contact with his children. Research in this area should definitely control for such factors. In addition, father-absent research almost consistently focuses on mothers and children. Consequently, we know very little about the "absent father."

Sharon Price-Bonham is an Associate Professor, and Joe F. Pittman is a Ph.D. Candidate in the Department of Child and Family Development, University of Georgia, Athens, GA 30602. Charles O. Welch is an NIMH Post-Doctoral Fellow, Department of Sociology, Washington State University. This project was funded by the College of Home Economics, University of Georgia, Athens, GA 30602.

0613-9641/81/1500-0264$00.95

There also appeared to be an increased emphasis on father-daughter incest. In fact, the majority of articles published which focus on father-daughter relationships deal with incest. This could be the result of the problem oriented focus of research and programs. However, it should be empasized father-daughter relationships are multi-faceted and other areas should be researched.

This bibliography includes references based on empirical research as well as other articles containing information on fathers. Major social science journals were reviewed, colleagues were contacted, and computer searches with CIJE and ERIC were undertaken. In addition, Sociological and Psychological Abstracts were reviewed. (It was necessary to examine works in some detail since fathers were often not included in works concerned with "parents.") After these searches it was decided to limit this bibliography to published works related to fathers in the U.S. (Therefore, dissertations and papers presented at professional meetings and unpublished reports were not included.)

References were classified according to their major themes or purposes. There are 14 major categories and an additional category which contains miscellaneous references. These categories are as follows:

1. General Literature Related to Fathers
2. Fathers and Pregnancy
3. Fathers and Their Children: Fathers and Their Families
4. Fathers and Daughters
5. Fathers and Sons
6. Young Fathers
7. Ethnic Minority Fathers
8. The Work Role and SES of Fathers
9. Fathers Divorcing and Divorced
10. Father Absence
11. Single Fathers
12. The Remarried Father and Stepfathers
13. Problems in Relation to Fathers
14. The Father and Applied Programs
15. Other Literature Related to Fathers

BOOKS AND CHAPTERS IN BOOKS

Atkin E, Rubin E: *Part-Time Father: A Guide For the Divorced Father.* New York, New American Library, 1976.

Berman C: *Making It as a Stepparent: New Roles—New Rules.* Garden City, NY, Doubleday, 1980.

Biller H, Meredith D: *Father Power.* Garden City, New York, Doubleday, 1975.

Blechman E A, Manning M: A reward-cost analysis of the single-parent family. In E J Mash, L A Hamerlynck, L C Handy (Eds), *Behavior Modification and Families.* New York, Bruner/Mazel, 1976.

Bugg R: *A Father Shares How to Enrich Family Life*. Grand Rapids, MI, Baker Book House, 1980.

Burton J, Rosen M: *The Fatherhood Formula*. Canoga Park, CA, Major Books, 1976.

Cammarata J, Leighton F: *The Fun Book of Fatherhood*. Los Angeles, CA, Corwin, 1978.

Cannon-Bonventre K, Kahn J R: *The Ecology of Help-Seeking Behavior Among Adolescent Parents*. Palo Alto, CA, American Institutes for Research, 1979.

Capaldi F P, McRae B: *Stepfamilies: A Cooperative Responsibility*. New York, New Viewpoints, 1979.

Daley E A: *Father Feelings*. New York, William & Co., 1978.

Duberman L: *The Reconstituted Family: A Study of Remarried Couples and Their Children*. Chicago, Nelson-Hall, 1975.

Dubrin A J: *The New Husbands and How to Become One*. Chicago, Nelson-Hall, 1976.
Emery A: *Stepfamily*. Philadelphia, Westminster, 1980.

Furstenberg F F Jr.: *Unplanned Parenthood: The Social Consequences of Teenage Childbearing*. New York, Free Press, 1979.

Galper M: *Co-Parenting: Sharing Your Child Equally. A Source Book for the Separated or Divorced Family*. Philadelphia, Running Press, 1979.

Gatley R, Koulack D: *Single Father's Handbook*. Garden City, 1979.

Gilbert S D: *What Is a Father For? A Father's Guide to the Pleasures and Problems of Parenthood with Advice From the Experts*. New York, Parent Magazine Press, 1975.

Green M: *Life Without Fathering*. New York, McGraw-Hill, 1977.

Gresh S: *Becoming a Father: A Handbook for Expectant Fathers*. New York, Butterick, 1980.

Hale N C: *The Birth of a Family: The New Role of the Father in Childbirth*. Garden City, NY, Doubleday, 1979.

Hamilton M L: *Father's Influence on Children*. Chicago, Nelson-Hall, 1977.

Heiderbrecht P, Rohrbach J: *Fathering a Son*. Evanston, IL, Moody Press, 1979.

Kahan S: *Expectant Father's Survival Kit*. New York, Sovereign, 1979.

Kahan S: *For Divorced Fathers Only*. New York, Sovereign, 1979.

Kitzinger S: *Giving Birth: The Parents Emotions in Childbirth*. New York, Schocken, 1978.

Lamb M: *The Role of the Father in Child Development*. New York, Wiley, 1976.

Levine J A: *Who Will Raise the Children? New Options for Fathers (and Mothers)*. New York, Lippincott, 1976.

Lucarini S: *The Difficult Role of the Father*. Brooklyn, New City, 1979.

MacDonald G: *The Effective Father*. Wheaton, IL, Tyndale, 1979.

MacDonald G: *Action Guide for the Effective Father*. Wheaton, IL, Tyndale, 1979.

Mayle P: *How to Be a Pregnant Father*. Secaucus, NJ, Lyle Stuart, 1977.

McFadden M: *Bachelor Fatherhood*. New York, Ace, 1978.

Pedersen F A (Ed): *The Father-Infant Relationship: Observational Studies in Family Settings*. New York, Praeger, 1980.

Phillips C R, Anzalone J T: *Fathering: Participation in Labor and Birth*. St. Louis, Mosby, 1976.

Pinegar E J: *Fatherhood*. Salt Lake City, Deseret, 1976.

Preston W H (Ed): *Fathers Are Special*. Nashville, TN, Broadman, 1977.

Reynolds W: *The American Father: Himself, His Woman, His Child*. New York, Paddington, 1978.

Rice F P: *Stepparenting*. Westport, CT, Condor, 1979.

Roosevelt R: *Living in Step*. New York, McGraw-Hill, 1979.

Rosenbaum V, Rosenbaum J: *Stepparenting*. Novato, CA, Chandler & Sharp, 1977.

Rosenthal K M, Keshet H F: *Fathers Without Partners: A Study of Fathers and the Family After Marital Separation*. Totowa, NJ, Rowman & Littlefield, 1980.

Rue J, Shanahan L: *Daddy's Girl, Mama's Boy*. New York, New American Library, 1979.

Shedd C: *The Best Dad Is a Good Lover*. Fairway, KS, Andrews & McMeel, 1977.

Shedd C: *A Dad Is For Spending Time With*. Fairway, KS, Andrews & McMeel, 1978.

Shepard M A, Goldman G: *Divorced Dads: Their Kids, Ex-Wives and New Lives*. Radnor, PA, Chilton, 1979

Stanley C F: *A Man's Touch*. Wheaton, IL, Victor, 1977.

Stein E V: *Fathering: Fact or Fable?* Nashville, TN, Abingdon, 1977.

Steinberg D: *Father Journal: Five Years of Awakening to Fatherhood*. Albion, CA, Times Change, 1977.

Sullivan S A: *The Fathers Almanac*. Garden City, NY, Doubleday, 1980.

Trunnel T: A review of studies of the psychosocial significance of the absent father. In H I McCubbin, B B Dahl, & E J Hunter (Eds), *Families in the Military System*. Beverly Hills, CA, Sage, 1976.

Visher E B, Visher J S: *Stepfamilies: A Guide to Working with Stepparents and Stepchildren*. New York, Brunner/Mazel, 1979.

Visher B B, Visher J S; *Stepfamilies: Myths and Realities*. Secaucus, NJ, Lyle Stuart, 1980.

Weiss R: *Marital Separation*. New York, Basic Books, 1975.

Woolley P: *The Custody Handbook*. New York, Simon & Schuster, 1980.

Zitner R, Hayden S: *Our Youngest Parents: Teenagers*. New York, Child Welfare League of America, 1980.

1. GENERAL LITERATURE RELATED TO FATHERS

Booth A, Edwards J N: Fathers: The invisible parent. *Sex Roles: A Journal of Research 6:* 445-456, 1980.

Broderick C B: Fathers. *Family Coordinator 26:* 269-275, 1977.

DeLissovoy V: Comments on the keeping fathers of America. *Family Coordinator 25:* 393-395, 1976.

Goldstein M Z: Fathering: A neglected activity. *American Journal of Psychoanalysis 37:* 325-336, 1977.

Lamb M E: Fathers: Forgotten contributors to child development. *Human Development 18:* 245-266, 1975.

Leacock E: The changing family and Levi-Strauss, or whatever happened to fathers. *Social Research 44:* 235-259, 1977.

Lewis R A, Pleck J H: Men's roles in the family. *Family Coordinator 28:* 429-432, 1979.

Maxwell J W: The keeping fathers of America. *Family Coordinator 25:* 387-392, 1976.

Perrucci C C: Determinants of male family-role performance. *Psychology of Women Quarterly 3:* 53-66, 1978.

Pleck J H: The male sex role: Definitions, problems, and sources of change. *Journal of Social Issues 32:* 155-164, 1976.

Rich A: The kingdom of the fathers. *Partisan Review 43:* 17-37, 1976.

Sussman M B: The family today: Is it an endangered species? *Children Today 27:* 37-47, 1977.

Swartz R: A father's view. *Children Today 6:* 14-17, 1976.

2. FATHERS AND PREGNANCY

Anderson S G: Abortion and the husband's consent. *Journal of Family Law 13:* 311-331, 1973-74.

Barnhill L, Rubenstein G, Rocklin N: From generation to generation: Fathers-to-be in transition. *Family Coordinator 28:* 229-235, 1979.

Bieber I, Bieber T B: Postpartum reactions in men and women. *Journal of the American Academy of Psychoanalysis 6:* 511-519, 1978.

Cavenar J O, Butts N T: Fatherhood and emotional illness. *American Journal of Psychiatry 134:* 429-431, 1977.

Coley S B, James B E: Delivery: A trauma for fathers. *Family Coordinator 25:* 359-363, 1976.

Fein R A: Men's entrance to parenthood. *Family Coordinator 25:* 341-347, 1976.

Frodi A M, Lamb M E: Father's and mother's responses to the faces and cries of normal and premature infants. *Developmental Psychology 14:* 490-498, 1979.

Gearing J: Facilitating the birth process and father-child bonding. *Counseling Psychologist 7:* 53-56, 1978.

Goldbach V: The right to an abortion—problems with parental and spousal consent. *New York School Law Review 22:* 65-86, 1976.

Gurwitt A R: Aspects of prospective fatherhood: A case report. *Psychoanalytic Study of the Child 31:* 237-271, 1976.

Hersh S P, Levin K: How love begins between parent and child. *Children Today 7:* 2-6, 1978.

Hott J R: The crisis of expectant fatherhood. *American Journal of Nursing 76:* 1436-1440, 1976.

Jeffcoate J A, Humphrey M E, Lloyd J K: Role perception and responses to stress in fathers and mothers following pre-term delivery. *Social Science and Medicine 13A:* 139-145, 1979.

Marquart R K: Expectant fathers: What are their needs? *MCN, The American Journal of Maternal Child Nursing 1:* 32-36, 1976.

Obrzut L A J: Expectant fathers' perception of fathering. *American Journal of Nursing 76:* 1440-1442, 1976.

Ogg E: What about the prospective father? *Today's Education 67:* 77-79, 1977.

Shostak A B: Abortion as fatherhood lost: Problems and reforms. *Family Coordinator 28:* 569-574, 1979.

Soule B, Standly K, Copans S A: Father identity. *Psychiatry 42:* 255-263, 1979.

Summer G: Giving expectant parents the help they need: The ABC's of prenatal education. *MCN, The American Journal of Maternal Child Nursing 1:* 220-225, 1976.

Wapner J: The attitudes, feelings, and behaviors of expectant fathers attending Lamaze classes. *Birth and the Family Journal 3:* 5-13, 1976.

Wente A S, Crockenberg S B: Transition to fatherhood: Lamaze preparation, adjustment difficulty and the husband-wife relationship. *Family Coordinator 25:* 351-357, 1976.

Wilson J P: Fetal experimentation: Rights of the father and questions of personhood. *Villanova Law Review 22:* 403-417, 1976-1977.

3. FATHERS AND THEIR CHILDREN:
FATHERS AND THEIR FAMILIES

Acock A C, Bengtson V L: On the relative influence of mothers and fathers: A covariance analysis of political and religious socialization. *Journal of Marriage and the Family 40:* 519-530, 1978.

Adams G R, Crane P: An assessment of parents' and teachers' expectations of preschool children's social preference for attractive or unattractive children and adults. *Child Development 51:* 224-231, 1980.

Adams G R, Lavoie J C: Parental expectations of educational and personal social performance and childrearing patterns as a function of attractiveness, sex, and conduct of the child. *Child Study Journal 5:* 125-142, 1975.

Aldous J: The search for alternatives: Parental behaviors and children's original problem solutions. *Journal of Marriage and the Family 37:* 711-722, 1975.

Balswick J O, Balkwell J W: Self-disclosure to same-and opposite-sex parents: An empirical test of insights from role theory. *Sociometry 40:* 282-286, 1977.

Bartz K W: Selected childrearing tasks and problems of mothers and fathers. *Family Coordinator 27:* 209-214, 1978.

Bearison D J: Sex-linked patterns of socialization. *Sex Roles 5:* 11-18, 1979.

Belsky J: Mother-father-infant interaction: A naturalistic observational study. *Developmental Psychology 15:* 601-607, 1979.

Bigner J J: Attitudes toward fathering and father-child activity. *Home Economics Research Journal 6:* 98-106, 1977.

Billingham R E, Walters J: Relationship between parent preference and peer preference among preadolescents. *Journal of Genetic Psychology 133:* 163-169, 1978.

Burke R J, Weir T: Working men as fathers of adolescents. *School Guidance Worker 33:* 4-9, 1977.

Clarke-Stewart K A: And daddy makes three: The father's impact on mother and young child. *Child Development 49:* 466-478, 1979.

Cohen D J, Dibble E, Grawe J M: Fathers' and mothers' perceptions of children's personality. *Archives of General Psychiatry 34:* 480-487, 1977.

Cohen D J, Dibble E, Grawe J M: Parental style. *Archives of General Psychiatry 34:* 445-451, 1977.

Cordell A S, Parke R D, Sawin D B: Fathers' views on fatherhood with special reference to infancy. *Family Relations 29:* 331-337, 1980.

Crano W D, Aronoff J: A cross-cultural study of expressive and instrumental role complementarity in the family. *American Sociological Review 43:* 463-471, 1978.

Dewinne R F, Overton T D, Schneider L J: Types produce types—Especially fathers. *Journal of Vocational Behavior 12:* 140-144, 1978.

Dickstein E B, Posner J M: Self-esteem and relationship with parents. *Journal of Genetic Psychology 133:* 273-276, 1978.

Dielman T E, Barton K, Cattell R B: Relationships among family attitudes and child rearing practices. *Journal of Genetic Psychology 130:* 105-112, 1977.

Epstein A S, Radin N: Motivational components related to father behavior and cognitive functioning in preschoolers. *Child Development 46:* 831-839, 1977.

Fein R A: The first weeks of fathering: The importance of choices and supports for new parents. *Birth and The Family Journal 3:* 53-58, 1976.

Fenton H: Lifestyles: Sharing our special baby. *Children Today 8:* 18-20, 1979.

Field T: Interaction behaviors of primary versus secondary caretaker fathers. *Developmental Psychology 14:* 183-184, 1978.

Galbraith G C, Crow C: Retrospective parental ratings and free associative sexual responsivity in male and female college students. *Psychological Reports 38:* 759-765, 1976.

Giattino J, Hogan J G: Analysis of a father's speech to his language-learning child. *Journal of Speech and Hearing Disorders 40:* 524-537, 1975.

Gilman R, Knox D: Coping with fatherhood: The first year. *Child Psychiatry and Human Development 6:* 134-148, 1976.

Golinkoff R M, Ames G J: A comparison of fathers' and mothers' speech with their young children. *Child Development 50:* 28-32, 1979.

Grotevant H D: Family similarities in interests and orientation. *Merrill-Palmer Quarterly 22:* 61-72, 1976.

Heath D H: Competent fathers: Their personalities and marriages. *Human Development 19:* 26-39, 1976.

Henggeler S W, Borduin C M, Rodick J D, Tavormina J B: Importance of task content for family interaction research. *Developmental Psychology 15:* 660-661, 1979.

Hillman L, Raskinn M, Orloffkaplan K: The liberated husband-father or babysitter? *Intellect 106:* 462-465, 1978.

Hobbs D F, Cole S P: Transition to parenthood: A decade replication. *Journal of Marriage and the Family 38:* 723-731, 1976.

Hobbs D F, Wimbish J M: Transition to parenthood by black couples. *Journal of Marriage and the Family 39:* 677-689, 1977.

Hock E, McKenry P C, Hock M D, Triolo S, Stewart L: Child's school entry: A stressful event in the lives of fathers. *Family Relations 29:* 467-472, 1980.

Hopkins P E: Every father should be a nursery school mother at least once in his life. *Young Children 32:* 26-29, 1977.

Jacobsen R, Berry K J, Olson K F: An empirical test of the generation gap: A comparative intrafamily study. *Journal of Marriage and the Family 37:* 841-852, 1975.

Jacob T: Verbal activity of middle-and lower-class parents when teaching their child. *Psychological Reports 40:* 575-578, 1977.

Johnson M M: Fathers, mothers and sex typing. *Sociological Inquiry 45:* 15-26, 1975.

Jordan B E: Parental behavior and intellectual functioning in preschool boys and girls. *Developmental Psychology 11:* 407-408, 1975.

Kemper T D, Reichler M L: Father's work integration and types and frequencies of rewards and punishments administered by fathers and mothers to adolescent sons and daughters. *Journal of Genetic Psychology 129:* 207-219, 1976.

Kemper T D, Reichler M L: Marital satisfaction and conjugal power as determinants of intensity and frequency of rewards and punishments administered by parents. *Journal of Genetic Psychology 129:* 221-234, 1976.

Kidder S J, Kuethe J L: Children's parental schemata as related to reading achievement. *Perceptual and Motor Skills 40:* 971-973, 1975.

Kirkpatrick S W: Sex-role classifications of adolescents: Relationship to actual and perceived parental types. *Journal of Genetic Psychology 135:* 237-244, 1978.

Lamb M E: The sociability of two-year-olds with their mothers and fathers. *Child Pychiatry and Human Development 5:* 182-188, 1975.

Lamb M E: Effects of stress and cohort on mother-and father-infant interaction. *Developmental Psychology 12:* 435-443, 1976.

Lamb M E: Parent-infant interaction in 8-month-olds. *Child Psychiatry and Human Development 7:* 56-63, 1976.

Lamb M E: Twelve-month-olds and their parents: Interaction in laboratory playroom. *Developmental Psychology 12:* 237-244, 1976.

Lamb M E: The development of mother-infant and father-infant attachments in the second year of life. *Developmental Psychology 13:* 637-648, 1977.

Lamb M E: Father-infant and mother-infant interaction in the first year of life. *Child Development 48:* 167-181, 1977.

Lamb M E: A re-examination of the infant social world. *Human Development 20:* 65-85, 1977.

Lamb M E: Paternal influences and the father's role: A personal perspective. *American Psychologist 34:* 938-943, 1979.

Lamb M E, Lamb J E: The nature and importance of the father-infant relationship. *Family Coordinator 25:* 378-384, 1976.

Lamb M E, Stevenson M B: Father-infant relationships: Their nature and importance. *Youth and Society 9:* 277-298, 1978.

Larson L E: Multilevel family interpersonal perception of ideal marital roles: An exploratory study. *Journal of Comparative Family Studies 6:* 223-237, 1975.

Lerner H E: Effects of the nursing mother-infant dyad on the family. *American Journal of Orthopsychiatry 49:* 339-348, 1979.

Lerner R M, Knapp J R: Actual and perceived intrafamilial attitudes of late adolescents and their parents. *Journal of Youth and Adolescence 4:* 17-36, 1975.

Lewis R A, Freneau P J, Roberts C L: Fathers and the postparental transition. *Family Coordinator 28:* 514-520, 1979.

Loeb R C, Horst L, Horton P J: Family interaction patterns associated with self-esteem in preadolescent girls and boys. *Merrill-Palmer Quarterly 26:* 205-217, 1980.

Lynn D B: Fathers and sex-role development. Family Coordinator 25: 403-408, 1976.

Mackey W C, Day R D: Some indicators of fathering behaviors in the United States: A cross-cultural examination of adult male-child interaction. *Journal of Marriage and the Family 41:* 287-299, 1976.

Main M H: Fathers' night in the kindergarten. *Day Care and Early Education 5;* 18-20, 1978.

Manion J: A study of fathers and infant caretaking. *Birth and the Family Journal 4:* 174-179, 1977.

Marcus R F: The child as elicitor of parental sanctions for independent and dependent behavior: A simulation of parent-child interaction. *Developmental Psychology 11:* 443-452, 1975.

Marcus R F: The effects of children's emotional and instrumental dependent behavior on parental response. *Journal of Psychology 92:* 57-63, 1976.

Margolin G, Patterson G R: Differential consequences provided by mothers and fathers for their sons and daughters. *Developmental Psychology 11:* 537-538, 1975.

Masur E F, Gleason J B: Parent-child interaction and the acquisition of lexical information during play. *Developmental Psychology 16:* 404-409, 1980.

McDonald D L: Paternal behavior at first contact with the newborn in a birth environment without intrusions. *Birth and the Family Journal 5:* 123-132, 1978.

McLaughlin B, Schutz C, White D: Parental speech to five-year-old children in a game-playing situation. *Child Development 51:* 580-582, 1980.

Mobley E D: Ego-ideal themes in fatherhood. *Smith College Studies in Social Work 45:* 230-252, 1975.

Ollendick D G: Parental locus of control and the assessment of children's personality characteristics. *Journal of Personality Assessment 43:* 401-405, 1979.

Olneck M R, Crouse J: The IQ meritocracy reconsidered: Cognitive skill and adult success in the United States. *American Journal of Education 88:* 1-31, 1979.

Parke R D: The father's role in infancy: A re-evaluation. *Birth and the Family Journal 5:* 211-213, 1978.

Parke R D, Sawin D B: The father's role in infancy: A re-evaluation. *Family Coordinator 25:* 365-371, 1976.

Peterson C, Peterson J: Issues concerning collaborating careers. *Journal of Vocational Behavior 7:* 173-180, 1975.

Peterson G H, Mehl L E, Leiderman P H: The role of some birth-related variables in father attachment. *American Journal of Orthopsychiatry 49:* 330-338, 1979.

Pines D: On becoming a parent. *Journal of Child Psychotherapy 4:* 19-31, 1978.

Prall R C: The role of the father in the preoedipal years. *Journal of the American Psychoanalytic Association* 28: 143-161, 1978.

Rendina I, Dickersheid J D: Father involvement with first-born infants. *Family Coordinator 25:* 373-378, 1976.

Robinson L L, Price-Bonham S: Father's reinforcement and task persistence of young children. *Journal of Psychology 19:* 83-91, 1978.

Ross G, Kagan J, Zelazo P, Kotelchuck M: Separation protest in infants in home and laboratory. *Developmental Psychology 11:* 256-257, 1975.

Russell G: The father role and its relation to masculinity, femininity, and androgyny. *Child Development 49:* 1174-1181, 1976.

Rypma C B: Biological bases of the paternal response. *Family Coordinator 25:* 335-339, 1976.

Sawin D B, Parke R D: Father's affectionate stimulation and caregiving behaviors with newborn infants. *Family Coordinator 28:* 509-513, 1979.

Schwab M R, Lundgren D C: Birth order, perceived appraisals by significant others, and self-esteem. *Psychological Reports 43:* 443-454, 1978.

Schwarzweller H K, Lyson T A: Some plan to become teachers: Determinants of career specification among rural youths in Norway, Germany, and the United States. *Sociology of Education 51:* 29-43, 1978.

Sinay R, Nihira K, Yusin A: Crisis in adolescence: Parental attitudes about children's behavior. *Psychological Reports 38:* 432-439, 1976.

Smart R C, Smart M S: Preadolescents' perceptions of parents and their relations to a test of responses to moral dilemmas. *Social Behavior and Personality 4:* 297-308, 1976.

Smith T E: Push versus pull: Intra-family versus peer-group variables as possible determinant of adolescent orientations toward parents. *Youth and Society 8:* 5-26, 1976.

Steinmetz S K: The use of force for resolving family conflict: The training ground for abuse. *Family Coordinator 26:* 19-26, 1977.

Tamayo A, Dugas A: Conceptual representation of mother, father, and God according to sex and field of study. *Journal of Psychology 97:* 79-84, 1977.

Tauber M A: Sex differences in parent-child interaction styles during a free-play session. *Child Development 30:* 81-88, 1979.

Thornburg H O: The male as a family role model. *Family Therapy 6:* 185-194, 1979.

Vaillant G E: Natural history of male psychological health: Correlates of successful marriage and fatherhood. *American Journal of Psychiatry 135:* 653-659, 1978.

Vandell D L: A microanalysis of toddlers' social interaction with mothers and fathers. *Journal of Genetic Psychology 134:* 299-312, 1979.

Vandewiele M: Perception of parent-adolescent relationships by secondary school students in Senegal. *Journal of Psychology 105:* 69-74, 1980.

Veron E L: Parental support of post-majority children in college: Changes and challenges. *Journal of Family Law 17:* 645-683, 1978-1979.

Viernstein M C, Hogan R: Parental personality factors and achievement motivation in talented adolescents. *Journal of Youth and Adolescence 4:* 183-190, 1975.

Walters J, Walters L H: Parent-child relationships: A review 1970-1979. *Journal of Marriage and the Family 42:* 807-824, 1980.

Watson J A, Kivett V R: Influences on the life satisfaction of older fathers. *Family Coordinator 25:* 482-488, 1976.

Weinraub M, Frankel J: Sex differences in parent-infant interaction during free play, departure, and separation. *Child Development 48:* 1240-1249, 1977.

Willerman L, Loehlin J C, Horn J M: Parental problem-solving speed as a correlate of intelligence in parents and their adopted and natural children. *Journal of Educational Psychology 71:* 627-634, 1979.

Weyant M E: Science and math fair for kids and dads. *Day Care and Early Education 7:* 26-28, 1979.

Wieting S G: An examination of intergenerational patterns of religious belief and practice. *Sociological Analysis 36:* 137-149, 1975.

Will C R, Stafford F P: Parental care of children: Time diary estimates of quantity, predictability, and variety. *Journal of Human Resources 15:* 219-239, 1980.

Williams T: Family resemblance in abilities: The Wechsler scales. *Behavior Genetics 5:* 405-409, 1975.

Wisdom J O: The role of the father in the mind of parents, in psychoanalytic theory and in the life of the infant. *International Review of Psycho-Analysis 3:* 231-239, 1976.

Wright B M, Zucker R A: Parental responses to competence and trauma in infants with reproductive casualty. *Journal of Abnormal Child Psychology 8:* 385-395, 1980.

Zey-Ferrell M, Tolone W L, Walsh R H: The intergenerational socialization of sex-role attitudes: A gender or generation gap? *Adolescence 13:* 95-108, 1978.

Ziegler R G, Musliner P J: Persistent themes: A naturalistic study of personality development in the family. *Family Process 16:* 293-305, 1977.

Zussman J U: Situational determinants of parental behavior: Effects of competing cognitive activity. *Child Development 51: 792-800, 1980.*

4. FATHERS AND DAUGHTERS

Bannon J A: Father-absent women: Self-concept and modes of relating to men. *Sex Roles: A Journal of Research 6:* 75-84, 1980.

Brook J S, Gordon A S, Brook D W: Perceived paternal relationships, adolescent personality, and female marijuana use. *Journal of Psychology 105:* 227-285, 1980.

Finkelhor D: Psychological, cultural and family factors in incest and family sexual abuse. *Journal of Marital and Family Therapy 63:* 41-49, 1980.

Gross M: Incestuous rape: A cause for hysterical seizures in four adolescent girls. *American Journal of Orthopsychiatry 49:* 704-708, 1979.

Gutheil T G, Avery N C: Multiple overt incest as family defense against loss. *Family Process 16:* 105-116, 1977.

Heilbrun A B: Identification with the father and sex-role development of the daughter. *Family Coordinator 25:* 411-416, 1976.

Hendrickson N J, Perkins D, White S, Buck T: Parent-daughter relationships in fiction. *Family Coordinator 24:* 257-265, 1975.

Herman J, Hirschmann L: Father-daughter incest. *Signs 2:* 735-756, 1977.

Kendis R J, Tan A L: Ego identity and perception of parents among female college students. *Perceptual and Motor Skills 47:* 1201-1202, 1978.

Lang D H, Papenfuhs R, Walters J: Delinquent females' perceptions of their fathers. *Family Coordinator 25:* 475-481, 1976.

Oliver L W: The relationship of parental attitudes and parent identification to career and homemaking orientation in college women. *Journal of Vocational Behavior 7:* 1-12, 1975.

Rosenfeld R A: Women's intergenerational occupational mobility. *American Sociological Review 43;* 36-46, 1978.

Spencer J: Father-daughter incest: A clinical view from the corrections field. *Child Welfare 57:* 581-590, 1978.

Stephens N, Day H D: Sex-role identity, parental identification, and self-concept of adolescent daughters from mother-absent, father-absent and intact families. *Journal of Psychology 103:* 193-202, 1978.

Vera F, Frances A: The incest taboo and family structure. *Family Process 15:* 235-244, 1976.

5. FATHER AND SONS

Awad G A: Father-son incest: A case report. *Journal of Nervous and Mental Disease 162:* 135-139, 1976.

Banker J R: Mourning a son: Childhood and paternal love in the consolateria of Gianozzo Manetti. *Journal of Psychohistory 3:* 351-362, 1976.

Barclay J R: Values in adolescent males and father-son relations. *Personnel and Guidance Journal 58:* 627-629, 1980.

Cavenar J O, Butts N T: Unconscious communication between father and son. *American Journal of Psychiatry 136:* 344-345, 1979.

Coughenour C M, Kowalski G S: Status and role of fathers and sons on partnership farms. *Rural Sociology 42:* 180-205, 1977.

Davis P H, Osherson A: Some effects of cultural stereotyping on fathering. *Journal of Contemporary Psychotherapy 10:* 32-38, 1978.

Dixon K N, Arnold L E, Calestro K: Father-son incest: Underreported psychiatric problem. *American Journal of Psychiatry 135:* 835-838, 1978.

Fallot R D, Mahl G F: Imitation in the family: A study of older parents and their adult sons. *International Journal of Aging and Human Development 7:* 1-14, 1976.

Grando R, Ginsberg B G: Communication in the father-son relationship: The parent-adolescent relationship development program. *Family Coordinator 25:* 465-473, 1976.

Grant T N, Domino G: Masculinity-feminity in fathers of creative male adolescents. *Journal of Genetic Psychology 129:* 19-27, 1976.

Heilbrun A B: Identification with the father and sex-role development of the daughter. *Family Coordinator 25:* 411-416, 1976.

Hunt L L, Hunt J G: Race and the father-son connection: The conditional relevance of father absence for the orientations and identities of adolescent boys. *Social Problems 23:* 35-52, 1975.

Jackson R M, Meara N M: Father identification, achievement, and occupational behavior of rural youth: 5-year follow-up. *Journal of Vocational Behavior 10:* 82-91, 1977.

Kowalski G S, Coughenour C M: Decision-making in joint agricultural operations. *Behavioural Sciences and Community Development 11:* 77-87, 1977.

Lynn D B: Fathers and sex-role development. *Family Coordinator 25:* 403-409, 1976.

Lytton H: The socialization of 2-year-old boys: Ecological findings. *Journal of Psychiatry and Allied Disciplines 17:* 287-304, 1976.

Lytton H: Disciplinary encounters between young boys and their mothers and fathers: Is there a contingency system? *Developmental Psychology 15:* 256-268, 1979.

Malina R M, Mueller W H, Holman J D: Parent-child correlations and heritability of stature in Philadelphia black and white children 6 to 12 years of age. *Human Biology 48:* 475-486, 1976.

Millen L, Roll S: Adolescent males' ratings of being understood by fathers, best friends and significant others. *Psychological Reports 40:* 1079-1082, 1977.

Millen L, Roll S: Relationships between sons' feelings of being understood by their fathers and measures of the sons' psychological functioning. *Journal of Genetic Psychology 130:* 19-25, 1977.

Pakizegi B: The interaction of mothers and fathers with their sons. *Child Development 49:* 479-482, 1978.

Reis M, Gold D: Relation of paternal availability to problem solving and sex-role orientation in young boys. *Psychological Reports 40:* 823-829, 1977.

Roll S, Millen L: Adolescent males' feeling of being understood by their fathers as revealed through clinical interviews. *Adolescence 13:* 83-94, 1978.

Schneider R J, Kojak G, Ressdorf H: Father-distance and drug abuse in young men. *Journal of Nervous and Mental Disease 165:* 269-274, 1977.

Smith R M, Walters J: Delinquent and non-delinquent males' perceptions of their fathers. *Adolescence 13:* 21-28, 1978.

Sullivan N D, Fleshman R P: Paternal deprivation in male heroin addicts. *Drug Forum 5:* 75-79, 1975-76.

Tucker L S, Cornwall T P: Mother-son *folie a deux:* A case of attempted patricide. *American Journal of Psychiatry 134:* 1146-1147, 1977.

Vandell D L: Effects of a play group experience on mother-son and father-son interaction. *Developmental Psychology 15:* 379-385, 1979.

Waterman C K, Waterman A S: Fathers and sons: A study of ego identity across two generations. *Journal of Youth and Adolescence 4:* 331-338, 1975.

Whaley-Klahn M A, Loney J: A multivariate study of the relationship of parental management to self-esteem and initial drug abuse in hyperkinetic/MBD boys. *Psychology in the Schools 14:* 485-492, 1977.

6. YOUNG FATHERS

Earls F, Siegel B: Precocious fathers. *American Journal of Orthopsychiatry 50:* 469-480, 1980.

Furstenberg F F, Jr: The social consequences of teenage parenthood. *Family Planning Perspectives 8:* 148-164, 1976.

Furstenberg F F, Jr, Talvitie K G: Children's names and paternal claims: Bonds between unmarried fathers and their children. *Journal of Family Issues 1:* 31-55, 1980.

Goldmeier H: School-age parents and the public schools. *Children Today 5:* 18-20, 36. 1976.

Knowles L W: High schools, marriage and the Fourteenth Amendment. *Journal of Family Law 11:* 711-736, 1972.

Leashore B R: Human services and the unmarried father: The"forgotten half." *Family Coordinator 28:* 529-534, 1979.

Lorenzi E M, Klerman L V, Jekel J F: School-age parents: How permanent a relationship? *Adolescence 12:* 13-22, 1977.

Pannor R, Evans B W: The unmarried father revisited. *Journal of School Health 45:* 286-291, 1975.

Parke R D, Power T G, Fisher T: The adolescent father's impact on the mother and child. *Journal of Social Issues 36:* 88-106, 1980.

Pfuhl E H, Jr: The unwed father: A "non-deviant" rule breaker. *Sociological Quarterly 19:* 113-128, 1978.

Plionis B M: Adolescent pregnancy: Review of the literature. *Social Work 20:* 302-307, 1975.

Poulin A B: Illegitimacy and family privacy: A note on maternal cooperation in paternity suits. *Northwestern University Law Review 70:* 910-932, 1976.

Rothstein A A: Adolescent males, fatherhood, and abortion. *Journal of Youth and Adolescence 7:* 203-214, 1978.

Sawin D B, Parke R D: Adolescent fathers: Some implications from recent research on paternal roles. *Educational Horizons 55:* 38-43, 1976.

7. ETHNIC MINORITY FATHERS

Adams P L, Horovitz J H: Psychopathology and fatherlessness in poor boys. *Child Psychiatry and Human Development 10:* 135-143, 1980.

Badaines J: Identification, imitation, and sex-role preference in father-present and father-absent black and chicano boys. *Journal of Psychology 92:* 15-24, 1976.

Cazenave N A: Middle-income black fathers: An analysis of the provider role. *Family Coordinator 28:* 583-593, 1979.

Cobas J A: Status consciousness and leftism: A study of Mexican-American adolescents. *Social Forces 55:* 1028-1042, 1977.

Dance D C: Daddy may bring home some bread, but he don't cut no ice: The economic plight of the father figure in black American literature. *Journal of Afro-American Issues 3:* 297-308, 1975.

Glautz D: Family structure, fate control, and counter-normative political beliefs among lower-class black students. *College Student Journal 10:* 121-125, 1976.

Jarman C: Education as a dimension of status incongruence between parents and the self perceptions of college students. *Sociology of Education 49:* 218-22, 1976.

Johnson L B, Staples R E: Family planning and the young minority male: A pilot project. *Family Coordinator 28:* 535-543, 1979.

Lecorgne L L, Laosa L M: Father absence in low-income Mexican-American families: Children's social adjustment and conceptual differentiation of sex role attributes. *Developmental Psychology 12:* 470-471, 1976.

Levine E S, Bartz K W: Comparative child-rearing attitudes among chicano, anglo, and black parents. *Hispanic Journal of Behavioral Sciences 1:* 165-178, 1979.

Martinez J L, Jr., Martinez S R, Olmedo E L, Goldman R D: The semantic differential technique: A comparison of chicano and anglo high school students. *Journal of Cross-Cultural Psychology 7:* 325-334, 1976.

McAdoo J L: Father-child interaction patterns and self-esteem in black preschool children. *Young Children 34:* 46-53, 1979.

Newby T J, Robinson P W, Hill R D: Preferences of Mexican-American children for parents or television. *Journal of Psychology 105:* 239-246, 1980.

Orive R, Gerard H B: Social contact of minority parents and their children's acceptance by classmates. *Sociometry 38:* 518-524, 1975.

Price-Bonham S, Skeen P: A comparison of black and white fathers with implications for parent education. *Family Coordinator 28:* 53-59, 1979.

Rubin R H: Matriarchal themes in black family literature: Implications for family life education. *Family Coordinator 27:* 33-39, 1978.

Scott J W: Polygamy: A futuristic family arrangement among African-Americans. *Black Books Bulletin 4:* 13-19, 1976.

Wilkinson C B, O'Connor W A: Growing up male in a black single-parent family. *Psychiatric Annals 7:* 50-59, 1977.

8. THE WORK ROLE AND SES OF FATHERS

Elliott F R: Occupational commitments and paternal deprivation. *Child Care, Heath and Development 4:* 305-315, 1978.

Fogelman K R, Goldstein H: Social factors associated with changes in educational attainment between 7 and 11. *Educational Studies 2:* 95-109, 1976.

Garfinkel J, Selvin S: A multivariate analysis of the relationship between parental age and birth order and the human secondary sex ratio. *Journal of Biosocial Science 8:* 113-121, 1976.

Goyder J C, Curtis J E: A three-generational approach to trends in occupational mobility. *American Journal of Sociology 81:* 129-138, 1975.

Jarmon C: Education as a dimension of status incongruence between parents and the self perceptions of college students. *Sociology of Education 49:* 218-222, 1976.

Jones S: The study of inter-generational social mobility: Past problems and directions for future research. *Case Western Reserve Journal of Sociology 7:* 32-45, 1975.

Larson D L, Spreitzer E A, Snyder E E: Social factors in the frequency of romantic involvement among adolescents. *Adolescence 11:* 7-12, 1976.

Marcum J P, Tienda M: A canonical correlation analysis of occupational mobility among Mexican-Americans. *Sociological Quarterly 19:* 439-449,1978.

Mascie-Taylor C G, Gibson J B: Social mobility and I Q components. *Journal of Biosocial Science* *10:* 263-276, 1978.

Moen P: Family impacts of the 1975 recession: Duration of unemployment. *Journal of Marriage and the Family 41:* 561-572, 1979.

Mortimer J T: Social class, work and the family: Some implications of the father's occupation for familial relationships and son's career decisions. *Journal of Marriage and the Family 38:* 241-256, 1976.

Scheck D C, Emerick R: The young male adolescent's perception of early childrearing behavior: The differential effects of socioeconomic status and family size. *Sociometry 39:* 39-52, 1976.

Spanier G B: Measuring social class among college students: A research note. *Adolescence 44:* 541-548, 1976.

Spencer W A: Interpersonal influences on educational aspirations: A cross-cultural analysis. *Sociology of Education 49:* 41-46, 1976.

Strong S R: Who gets financial aid? *Research Bulletin 16:* 1-19, 1975.

Sugiyama T, Bock E W, Berardo F M: Social status, mobility, illegitimacy and subsequent marriage. *Journal of Marriage and the Family 37:* 643-654, 1975.

Suri S, Verma P: The relationship between fathers' and children's attitudes towards social change at three levels of socio-economic status. *Journal of Psychological Researches 21:* 52-55, 1977.

Vanfossen B E: Sexual stratification and sex-role socialization. *Journal of Marriage and the Family 39:* 563-574, 1977.

9. FATHERS: DIVORCING AND DIVORCED

Abarbanel A: Shared parenting after separation and divorce: A study of joint custody. *American Journal of Orthopsychiatry 49:* 320-329, 1979.

Colletta N D: The impact of divorce: Father absence or poverty? *Journal of Divorce 3:* 27-35, 1979.

Cullen F T, Heiner K W, Sullo P: Child support collection: A stick-and-carrot approach. *Social Work 25:* 397-402, 1980.

DeSimone-Luis J, O'Mahoney K, Hunt D: Children of separation and divorce: Factors influencing adjustment. *Journal of Divorce 3:* 37-42, 1979.

Dominic K T, Schlesinger B: Weekend fathers: Family shadows. *Journal of Divorce 3:* 241-247, 1980.

Dreyfus E A: Counseling the divorced father. *Journal of Marriage and Family Therapy 5:* 79-85, 1979.

Finkelstein K, Rosenthal K M: Single-parent fathers: A new study. *Children Today 7:* 13-19, 1978.

Friedman H J: The father's parenting experience in divorce. *American Journal of Psychiatry* 1177-1182, 1980.

Fulton J A: Parental reports of children's post-divorce adjustment. *Journal of Social Issues 35:* 126-139, 1979.

Glick P C: Children of divorced parents in demographic perspective. *Journal of Social Issues 35:* 170-182, 1979.

Grief J B: Fathers, children, and joint custody. *American Journal of Orthopsychiatry 49:* 311-319, 1979.

Hess R D, Camara K A: Post-divorce family relationships as mediating factors in the consequences of divorce for children. *Journal of Social Issues 35:* 79-96, 1979.

Hetherington E M: Divorce: A child's perspective. *American Psychologist 34:* 851-858, 1979.

Hetherington E M, Cox M, Cox R: The aftermath of divorce. In J H Stevens, Jr, M Mathews (Eds), *Mother-child, Father-child relations.* Washington, D. C., National Association for the Education of Young Children, 1978.

Hetherington E M, Cox M, Cox R: Divorced fathers. *Family Coordinator 25:* 417-428, 1976.

Hozman T L, Froiland D J: Families in divorce: A proposed model for counseling the children. *Family Coordinator 25:* 271-275, 1976.

Kelly J B, Wallerstein J S: Children of divorce. *National Elementary Principal 59:* 51-58, 1979.

Keshet H F, Rosenthal K M: Fathering after marital separation. *Social Work 23:* 11-18, 1978.

Kohn S D: Coping with family change. *National Elementary Principal 59:* 40-50, 1979.

Kurdek L A, Siesky A L: Divorced single parents' perceptions of child-related problems. *Journal of Divorce 1:* 361-369, 1978.

Kurdek L A, Siesky A L: Sex role self-concepts of single divorced parents and their children. *Journal of Divorce 3:* 249-261, 1980.

Kurdek L A, Siesky A L: An interview study of parents' perceptions of their children's reactions and adjustments to divorce. *Journal of Divorce 3:* 5-16, 1979.

Levitin T E: Children of divorce: An introduction. *Journal of Social Issues 35:* 1-25, 1979.

Lewis K: Single-parent families in rural communities. *Human Services in the Rural Environment 3:* 7-18, 1977.

Norton A J: The portrait of the one-parent family. *National Elementary Principal 59:* 32-35, 1979.

Parish T J, Dostal J W: Relationships between evaluations of self and parents by children from intact and divorced families. *Journal of Psychology 104:* 35-38, 1980.

Parish T S, Taylor J C: The impact of divorce and subsequent father absence on children's and adolescents' self-concepts. *Journal of Youth and Adolescence 8:* 427-432, 1979.

Price-Bonham S, Balswick J O: The noninstitutions: Divorce, desertion, and remarriage. *Journal of Marriage and the Family 42:* 959-972, 1980.

Ricci I: Divorce, remarriage and the schools. *Phi Delta Kappan 60:* 509-511, 1979.

Rosenthal P A: Sudden disappearance of one parent with separation and divorce: The grief and treatment of preschool children. *Journal of Divorce 3:* 43-53, 1979.

Salk L: On the custody rights of fathers in divorce. *Journal of Clinical Child Psychology 6:* 49-50, 1977.

Santrock J, Warshak R A: Father custody and social development in boys and girls. *Journal of Social Issues 35:* 112-125, 1979.

Smith J S: Alimony for men—The changing law. *Florida State University Law Review 7:* 687-700, 1979.

Snyder L: The deserting, nonsupporting father: Scapegoat of family nonpolicy. *Family Coordinator 28:* 594-598, 1979.

Spicer J W, Hampe G D: Kinship interaction after divorce. *Journal of Marriage and the Family 37:* 113-119, 1975.

Uslander A S: Divorce: You too must pay child support. *Learning 5:* 23-32, 1976.

Wallerstein J S, Kelly J B: Children and divorce: A review. *Social Work 24:* 468-474, 1979.

Wallerstein J S, Kelly J B: The effects of parental divorce: Experiences of the child in early latency. *American Journal of Orthopsychiatry 46:* 20-32, 1976.

Weiss R S: Going it alone. *National Elementary Principal 59:* 14-25, 1979.

Weiss R S: Growing up a little faster: The experience of growing up in a single-parent household. *Journal of Social Issues 35:* 97-111, 1979.

Wilkinson G S, Bleck R T: Children's divorce groups. *Elementary School Guidance and Counseling 11:* 205-212, 1977.

Wilson J T: Catering for single parents. *Teaching Adults 10:* 4-5, 1975.

Woody R H: Behavioral science criteria in child custody determinations. *Journal of Marriage and Family Counseling 3:* 11-18, 1977.

Woody R H: Fathers with child custody. *Counseling Psychologist 7:* 60-63, 1978.

10. FATHER ABSENCE

Adams P L, Horovitz J H: Coping patterns of mothers of poor boys. *Child Psychiatry and Human Development 10:* 144-155, 1980.

Austin R L: Race, father-absence, and female delinquency. *Criminology: An Interdisciplinary Journal 15:* 487-504, 1978.

Bales K B: The single parent family aspirations and academic achievement. *Southern Journal of Educational Research 13:* 145-160, 1979.

Bernstein B E: How father absence in the home affects the mathematics skills of fifth-graders. *Family Therapy 3:* 45-59, 1976.

Boone S L: Effects of fathers' absence and birth order on aggressive behavior of young male children. *Psychological Reports 44:* 1223-1229, 1979.

Boss P: A clarification of the concept of psychological father presence in families experiencing ambiguity of boundary. *Journal of Marriage and the Family 39:* 141-151, 1977.

Boss P: The relationship of psychological father presence, wife's personal qualities and wife/family dysfunction in families of missing fathers. *Journal of Marriage and the Family 42:* 541-549, 1980.

Boss P G, McCubbin H I, Lester G: The corporate executive wife's coping patterns in response to routine husband-father absence. *Family Process 18:* 79-86, 1979.

Carroll M P: Freud on homosexuality and the super-ego: Some cross-cultural tests. *Behavior Science Research 13:* 255-271, 1978.

Carter D E, Walsh J A: Father absence and the black child: A multivariate analysis. *Journal of Negro Education 49:* 134-143, 1980.

Cohen G: Absentee husbands in spiralist families. *Journal of Marriage and the Family 39:* 595-604, 1977.

Crook T, Raskin A: Association of childhood parental loss with attempted suicide and depression. *Journal of Consulting and Clinical Psychology 43:* 227, 1975.

Dahl B B, McCubbin H I, Lester G R: War-induced father absence: Comparing the adjustment of children in reunited, non-reunited and reconstituted families. *International Journal of Sociology of the Family 6:* 99-108, 1976.

Davidson C W: The prediction of drug use through discriminate analysis from variables common to potential secondary school dropouts. *Journal of Educational Research 72:* 313-316, 1979.

Duke M P, Lancaster W: A note on locus of control as a function of father absence. *Journal of Genetic Psychology 129:* 335-336, 1976.

Earl L, Lohmann N: Absent fathers and black male children. *Social Work 23:* 413-415, 1978.

Falk P L: One out of five and largely ignored. *National Elementary Principal 59:* 76-80, 1979.

Felthous A R: Aggression against cats, dogs and people. *Child Psychiatry and Human Development 10:* 169-177, 1980.

Fowler P C, Richards, H C: Father absence, educational preparedness, and academic achievement: A test of the confluence model. *Journal of Educational Psychology 70:* 595-601, 1978.

Freeman J: Women and urban policy. *Signs: Journal of Women in Culture and Society 5:* 4-12, 1980.

Gershansky I S, Hainline L, Goldstein H S: Maternal differentiation, onset and type of father's absence and psychological differentiation in children. *Perceptual and Motor Skills 46:* 1147-1152, 1978.

Grossberg S H, Crandall L: Father loss and father absence in preschool children. *Clinical Social Work Journal 6:* 123-134, 1978.

Hainline L, Feig, E: The correlates of childhood father absence in college-aged women. *Child Development 49:* 37-42, 1978.

Hillenbrand E D: Father absence in military families. *Family Coordinator 25:* 451-458, 1976.

Hunt J G, Hunt L L: Race, daughters and father-loss: Does absence make the girl grow stronger? *Social Problems 25:* 90-102, 1977.

Jenkins S: Children of divorce. *Children Today 1:* 16-20, 1978.

Johnson J: Help for the handicapped male child of the single parent. *Pointer 22:* 71-73, 1977.

Kagel S A, White R M Jr., Coyne J C: Father-present families of disturbed and nondisturbed adolescents. *Journal of Orthopsychiatry 48:* 342-352, 1978.

Kestenbaum C J, Stone M H: The effects of fatherless homes upon daughters: Clinical impressions regarding paternal deprivation. *Journal of the American Academy of Psychoanalysis 4:* 171-190, 1976.

Marino C D, McCowan R J; The effects of parent absence on children. *Child Study Journal 6:* 165-182, 1976.

McCarthy C: Mothers struggling on their own. *National Elementary Principal 55:* 52-53, 1976.

McCubbun H I, Dahl B B, Lester G R, Benson D, Robertson M L: Coping repertoires of families adapting to prolonged war-induced separations. *Journal of Marrriage and the Family 38:* 461-471, 1976.

McCubbin H I, Dahl B B, Lester G R, Ross B A: The returned prisoner of war: Factors in family reintegration. *Journal of Marriage and the Family 37:* 471-478, 1975.

McCubbin H I, Hunter E J, Dahl B B: Residuals of war: Families of prisoners of war and servicemen missing in action. *Journal of Social Issues 31:* 95-109, 1975.

Oshman H P, Manosevitz M: Death fantasies of father-absent and father-present late adolescents. *Journal of Youth and Adolescence 7:* 41-48, 1978.

Parish T S: The relationship between factors associated with father loss and individuals' level of moral judgment. *Adolescence 15:* 535-541, 1980.

Parish T S, Copeland T F: Locus of control and father loss. *Journal of Genetic Psychology 136:* 147-148, 1980.

Parker S, Smith J, Ginat J: Father absence and cross-sex identity: The puberty rites controversy revisited. *American Ethnologist 2:* 687-706, 1975.

Peck B B, Schroeder D: Psychotherapy with the father-absent military family. *Journal of Marriage and Family Counseling 2:* 23-30, 1976.

Pedersen F A: Does research on children reared in father-absent families yield information on father influences? *Family Coordinator 25:* 459-464, 1976.

Pedersen F A, Rubenstein J L, Yarrow L J: Infant development in father-absent families. *Journal of Genetic Psychology 135:* 51-61, 1979.

Roach D A: Effects of some social variables on field dependence. *Perceptual and Motor Skills 48:* 559-562, 1979.

Sack W H: Children of imprisoned fathers. *Psychiatry 40:* 163-174, 1977.

Sack W H, Seidler J, Thomas S: The children of imprisoned parents: A psychosocial exploration. *American Journal of Orthopsychiatry 46:* 618-628, 1976.

Salant E G: Johnny: A one-parent preschooler. *Art Education 33:* 22-24, 1980.

Santrock J W: Father absence, perceived maternal behavior, and moral development in boys. *Child Development 46:* 753-757, 1975.

Santrock J W: Effects of father absence on sex-typed behaviors in male children: Reason for the absence and age of onset of the absence. *Journal of Genetic Psychology 130:* 3-10, 1977.

Santrock J W, Tracy R L: Effects of children's family structure status on the development of stereotypes by teachers. *Journal of Educational Psychology 70:* 754-757, 1978.

Santrock J W, Warshak R A: Father custody and social development in boys and girls. *Journal of Social Issues 35:* 112-125, 1979.

Sauer R J: Absentee father syndrome. *Family Coordinator 28:* 245-249, 1979.

Savage J E, Jr., Adair A V, Friedman P: Community-social variables related to black parent-absent families. *Journal of Marriage and the Family 40:* 779-785, 1978.

Schaengold M: The relationship between father-absence and encopresis. *Child Welfare 56:* 386-394, 1977.

Schell L M, Courtney D: The effect of male teachers on the academic achievement of father-absent sixth grade boys. *Journal of Educational Research 72:* 194-196, 1979.

Sciara F J: Effects of father absence on the educational achievement of urban black children. *Child Study Journal 5:* 45-55, 1975.

Shinn M B: Father absence and children's cognitive development. *Psychological Bulletin 85:* 295-324, 1978.

Snyder L M: The deserting, nonsupporting father: Scapegoat of family nonpolicy. *Family Coordinator 28:* 594-598, 1979.

Solomon M A, Herch L B: Death in the family: Implications for family development. *Journal of Marital and Family Therapy 5:* 43-49, 1979.

Stolorow R D, Lachmann F M: Early object loss and denial: Developmental considerations. *Psychoanalytic Quarterly 44:* 596-611, 1975.

Sussman M B: What every school principal should know about families: An immodest proposal. *National Elementary Principal 55:* 32-41, 1976.

Vargon M M, Lynn D B, Barton K: Effects of father absence on women's perception of ideal mate and father. *Multivariate Experimental Clinical Research 2:* 33-42, 1976.

Wyschogrod E: Sons without fathers: A study in identity and culture. *Journal of the American Academy of Psychoanalysis 6:* 249-262, 1978.

11. SINGLE FATHERS

Bartz K W, Witcher W C: When father gets custody. *Children Today 7:* 2-6, 1978.

Bernstein B E: Lawyer and counselor as an interdiscipinary team: Preparing the father for custody. *Journal of Marital and Family Counseling 3:* 29-41, 1977.

Clay P L: The schools and single parents: Accessibility is the key. *NASSP Bulletin 64:* 40-43, 1980.

Gasser R D, Taylor C M: Role adjustment of single parent fathers with dependent children. *Family Coordinator 25:* 397-401, 1976.

Katz A J: Lone fathers: Perspectives and implications for family policy. *Family Coordinator 28:* 521-528, 1979.

Lagnese A, Green S: Discharge planning in foster care cases where the father is the significant parent. *Child Welfare 51:* 612-617, 1976.

Lewis K: Single-father families: Who they are and how they fare. *Child Welfare 57:* 643-651, 1978.

Lowenstein J S, Koopmen E J: A comparison of the self-esteem between boys living with single-parent mothers and single-parent fathers. *Journal of Divorce 2:* 195-208, 1978.

Mendes H A: Single fathers. *Family Coordinator 25:* 439-444, 1976.

Mendes H A: Single fatherhood. *Social Work 21:* 308-312, 1976.

Mendes H A: Single parent families: A typology of life-styles. *Social Work 24:* 193-200, 1979.

Orthner D K, Brown T, Ferguson D: Single-parent fatherhood: An emerging lifestyle. *Family Coordinator 25:* 429-437, 1976.

Palker P: How to deal with the single-parent child in the classroom. *Teacher 98:* 50-54, 1980.

Sametz L: Children of incarcerated women. *Social Work 25:* 298-303, 1980.

Seagull A A, Seagull E A: The non-custodial father's relationship to his child: Conflicts and solutions. *Journal of Clinical Child Psychology 6:* 11-15, 1977.

Schlesinger B: Single-parent fathers: A research review. *Children Today 7:* 12, 1978.

Schorr A L, Moen P: The single parent and public policy. *Social Policy 9:* 15-21, 1979.

Smith M J: The social consequences of single parenthood: A longitudinal perspective. *Family Relations 29:* 75-80, 1980.

12. REMARRIED FATHERS AND STEPFATHERS

Chapman M: Father absence, stepfathers, and the cognitive performance of college students. *Child Development 48:* 1155-1158, 1977.

Oshman H P, Manosevitz M: Father absence: Effects of stepfathers upon psychosocial development in males. *Developmental Psychology 12:* 479-480, 1976.

Parish T S, Copeland T F: The relationship between self-concepts and evaluations of parents and stepfathers. *Journal of Psychology 101:* 135-138, 1979.

Perkins T F, Kahan J P: An empirical comparison of natural-father and step-father family systems. *Family Process 18:* 175-183, 1979.

Rallings E M: The special role of stepfather. *Family Coordinator 25:* 445-448, 1976.

Wilson K L, Zurcher L A, McAdams D C, Curtis R L: Stepfathers and stepchildren: An exploratory analysis from two national surveys. *Journal of Marriage and the Family 37:* 526-536, 1975.

Yahraes H: Stepfathers as parents. Families Today: A research sampler on families and children NIMH Science Monographs 1, DHEW Publication No. (ADM) 79-815. Rockville, MD, U S Department of Health, Education, and Welfare *1:* 347-362, 1979.

13. PROBLEMS IN RELATION TO FATHERS

Abroms K I, Bennett J W: Current genetic and demographic findings in Down's Syndrome: How are they presented in college textbooks on exceptionality? *Mental Retardation 18:* 101-107, 1980.

Alexander B K, Dibb G S: Interpersonal perception in addict families. *Family Process 16:* 17-28, 1977.

Anable W R: Homicidal threat as grief work. *Psychiatric Opinion 15:* 43-47, 1978.

Cramblit N S, Siegel G M: The verbal environment of a language-impaired child. *Journal of Speech and Hearing Disorders 42:* 474-482, 1977.

Cummings S T: The impact of the child's deficiency on the father: A study of fathers of mentally retarded and of chronically ill children. *American Journal of Orthopsychiatry 46:* 246-255, 1976.

DeBoor M F: What is to become of Katherine? *Exceptional Children 41:* 517-518, 1975.

Dunner D L, Fieve R R: Psychiatric illness in fathers of men with bipolar primary affective disorder. *Archives of General Psychiatry 32:* 1134-1137, 1975.

Goldstein H S, Gershansky I: Psychological differentiation in clinic children. *Perceptual and Motor Skills 42:* 1159-1162, 1976.

Huttunen M O, Niskanen P: Prenatal loss of father and psychiatric disorders. *Archives of General Psychiatry 35:* 429-431,1978.

Jones M B, Borland B L: Social mobility and alcoholism: A comparison of alcoholics with their fathers and brothers. *Journal of Studies on Alcohol 36:* 62-68, 1975.

Justice B, Duncan D F: Child abuse as a work-related problem. *Corrective and Social Psychiatry and Journal of Behavior Technology, Methods and Therapy 23:* 53-55, 1977.

L'Abate L: Pathogenic role rigidity in fathers: Some observations. *Journal of Marital and Family Counseling 1:* 69-79, 1975.

Lenkowsky L K, Saposnek D T: Family consequences of parental dyslexia. *Journal of Learning Disabilities 11:* 59-65, 1978.

Mathews L J, Ilon L: Becoming a chronic runaway: The effects of race and family in Hawaii. *Family Relations 29:* 404-409, 1980.

Mercer G W, Kohn P M: Child-rearing factors, authoritarianism, drug use attitudes, and adolescent drug use: A model. *Journal of Genetic Psychology 136:* 159-172, 1980.

Mulder H C, Suurmeijer TPBM: Families with a child with epilepsy: A sociological contribution. *Journal of Biosocial Science 9:* 13-24, 1977.

Orvaschel H, Mednick S, Schulsinger F, Rock D: The children of psychiatrically disturbed parents: Differences as a function of the sex of the sick parent. *Archives of General Psychiatry 36:* 691-695, 1979.

Power P W: The chronically ill husband and father: His role in the family. *Family Coordinator 28:* 616-621, 1979.

Prendergast, T S, Jr., Schaefer E S: Correlates of drinking and drunkeness among high-school students. *Quarterly Journal of Studies on Alcohol 35:* 232-242, 1974.

Price-Bonham S, Addison S: Families and mentally retarded children: Emphasis on the father. *Family Coordinator 27:* 221-230, 1978.

Schuckit M A, Gunderson E K E, Heckman N A, Kolb D: Family history as a predictor of alcoholism in U.S. Navy personnel. *Journal of Studies on Alcohol 37:* 1678-1685, 1976.

Shumway J: Do you see what I see? *New Outlook for the Blind 69:* 377-379, 1975.

Slouth N M, Kogan K L, Tyler N B: Deprivation of parent norms for the Maryland parent attitude survey: Application to parents of developmentally delayed children. *Psychological Reports 42;* 183-189, 1978.

Summers F, Walsh F: Symbiosis and confirmation between father and schizophrenic. *American Journal of Orthopsychiatry 49:* 136-148, 1979.

Tucker L S, Jr: A comparison of the value preferences of emotionally disturbed adolescents and their parents with normal adolescents and their parents. *Adolescence 11:* 549-567, 1976.

Wilker L : A comment on families and mentally retarded children: Emphasis on the father. *Family Coordinator 28:* 421-424, 1979.

14. THE FATHER AND APPLIED PROGRAMS

Berg B, Rosenblum N: Fathers in family therapy: A survey of family therapists. *Journal of Marital and Family Counseling 3:* 85-91, 1977.

Brody S: Daddy's gone to Colorado: Male-staffed child care for father-absent boys. *Counseling Psychologist 7:* 33-36, 1978.

Garrigan J J, Bambrick A F: New findings in research on go-between process. *International Journal of Family Therapy 1:* 76-85, 1979.

Eversoll D: The changing father role: Implications for parent education programs for today's youth. *Adolescence 14:* 535-544, 1979.

Fein R A: Research on fathering: Social policy and an emergent perspective. *Journal of Social Issues 34:* 122-135, 1978.

Firestone P, Kelly M J, Fike S: Are fathers necessary in parent training groups? *Journal of Clinical Child Psychology 9:* 44-47, 1980.

Martin B: Brief family intervention: Effectiveness and the importance of including the father. *Journal of Consulting and Clinical Psychology 45:* 1002-1010, 1977.

Reiter G F, Kilmann P R: Mothers as family change agents. *Journal of Counseling Psychology 22:* 61-65, 1975.

Resnick J L, Resnick M B, Packer A B, Wilson J: Fathering classes: A psycho/educational model. *Counseling Psychologist 7:* 56-60, 1978.

Scoresby A L, Christensen B: Differences in interaction and environmental conditions of clinic and non-clinic families: Implications for counselors. *Journal of Marriage and Family Counseling 2:* 63-67, 1976.

Wallerstein J S, Kelly J B: Brief intervention with children in divorcing families. *American Journal of Orthopsychiatry 47:* 23-37, 1977.

Wallerstein J S, Kelly J B: Divorce counseling: A community service for families in the midst of divorce. *American Journal of Orthopsychiatry 47:* 4-22, 1977.

15. OTHER LITERATURE RELATED TO FATHERS

Bozett F W: Gay Fathers: How and why they disclose their homosexuality to their children. *Family Relations 29:* 173-179, 1980.

Eversoll D: A two generational view of fathering. *Family Coordinator 28:* 508-518, 1979.

Harrington E G: Presidents as parents—two studies. *Intercom 94-95:* 37-47, 1979.

Heath D H: Competent fathers: Their personalities and marriages. *Human Development 19:* 26-39, 1976.

Heath D H: What meaning and effects does fatherhood have for the maturing of professional men? *Merrill-Palmer Quarterly 24:* 265-278, 1978.

Hood J, Golden S: Beating time/making time: The impact of work scheduling on men's family roles. *Family Coordinator 28:* 575-582, 1979.

Krause H D: Children's rights and the uniform parentage act. *Law in American Society 4:* 15-20, 1975.

Krueger D W: Symptom passing in a transvestite father and three sons. *American Journal of Psychiatry 135:* 739-742, 1978.

Lagnese A, Green S: Discharge planning in foster care cases where the father is the significant parent. *Child Welfare 55:* 612-617, 1976.

Miller B: Gay fathers and their children. *Family Coordinator 28:* 544-552, 1979.

Rypma C B: Biological base of the paternal response. *Family Coordinator 25:* 335-339, 1976.

Seelbach W C: Gender differences in expectations for filial responsibility. *Gerontologist 17:* 421-425, 1977.

Todres R: Runaway wives: An increasing North-American phenomenon. *Family Coordinator 27:* 17-21, 1978.

Touliatours J, Lindholm B W: Factor analytic study of potential for foster parenthood. *Psychological Reports 41:* 86, 1977.

Townes B D, Ferguson W D, Gillam B: Differences in psychological sex, adjustment, and familial influences among homosexual and non-homosexual populations. *Journal of Homosexuality 1:* 261-272, 1976.

Watson J A, Kivett V R: Influences on the life satisfaction of older fathers. *Family Coordinator 25:* 482-488, 1976.

Infant Mental Health Journal, Vol. 2, No. 4, Winter 1981

Book Reviews

FATHERING: PARTICIPATION IN LABOR AND DELIVERY. Celeste R. Phillips, RN, MS and Joseph T. Anzalone, MD. St. Louis, C.V. Mosby Co., 1978 (151 pages; $8.95).

The authors intend their discussion of the father's role during the antepartum and intrapartum periods of childbearing to be useful as a "supplemental text for maternity nursing courses, obstetrical courses in medical schools, family life classes, and parenting classes." The extreme diversity of the proposed audience contributes to the feeling of not really knowing for whom the book is intended. Portions of the book obviously were directed at the father (or couple), while others used technical medical terminology, not easily understood by individuals lacking a professional level background in health care.

The book is divided into five units, the first three dealing with the father's historical role in childbearing, the physician's viewpoint regarding the father's involvement in labor and delivery, and a discussion of family centered maternity care. The final two units contain directly quoted reactions of fathers to the births of their infants.

The first unit of the book deals with the prospective father, and provides discussion of social, emotional, educational, and legislative issues concerning the development of the father's role in labor and birth during the 19th and 20th centuries. The unit traces the developing relationship of the father to his offspring, and the ways in which he participates (or is prevented from participating) in the events surrounding childbearing. Also discussed is the emotional effect of pregnancy on the prospective father as he prepares for the event of birth and his changing responsibilities within the developing family.

The unit identifies early legislation that allowed, if not encouraged, the father to share the labor and delivery experience with his spouse. Court decisions (one as late as 1974)

that blocked the father's access to the birth process also are presented. The authors discuss the issue of "husband" vs. "father" and note that this distinction continues to be used by many hospitals to block access to labor and delivery for unmarried fathers.

The last portion of unit one presents studies which provide support for father participation in the birthing experience, and the benefits to the family when the father does participate. Additionally, several studies are cited which address the effect that this participation has on father-infant attachment. The unit concludes with an extensive reference list containing timely and representative studies.

The second unit (written by Anzalone) deals with the father's involvement in childbirth from the physician's point of view. The author presents his own view of the importance of having fathers participate in childbirth, but essentially absolves all physicians who do not allow fathers to be involved. I found this dichotomy difficult to accept and question the authors' offering of "ammunition" to the physician who wishes to block the father's access for whatever reason. In fact, the author offers several reasons why fathers might be denied access to the birthing process.

Anzalone details the development of his philosophy of father involvement in labor and delivery. This section is of dubious value to the reader, and in fact, this entire unit lends little to the book. It also contains a mock interview with a father "off the street...who comes into the physician's office full of doubts and misgivings" about his participation in labor and birth. While some of the questions reflect typical responses of fathers, the way in which the interview is presented is stilted and unrealistic.

The author uses his own practice to outline the progression of childbirth preparation classes, and in this unit some helpful information is presented. He details a number of issues (nutrition, exercise, physiological and emotional changes) that should be part of any comprehensive educational program for childbearing couples.

The third unit discusses family centered maternity care, alternative birthing centers, and risk factors that would necessitate use of typical delivery room care. The first part of the unit is overdramatized and intimates that the routine hospital delivery is always stark and dehumanizing. By contrast, the alternative birthing center is characterized as warm, supportive and friendly. This section might cause some real concern for couples who have opted for hospital delivery, or couples for whom some risk in the mother or fetus will necessitate hospital delivery. Such simplistic overgeneralization is a disservice to hospital personnel, most of whom in fact are committed to providing a supportive environment for the families they serve.

The final part of unit three will be all but incomprehensible to individuals with no health background. It details high-risk factors which necessitate hospital delivery, but the terminology used limits the usefulness of the material for parents and lay childbirth educators. This material may have been more effectively placed in an appendix (or even deleted) since it bears little relationship to the main topic the unit purports to address.

The last two units which make up more than half the book, contain fathers' descriptions of the birth of their infants. Many of these reminiscences are very sensitive and emotional responses to participating in a process that obviously affected the fathers greatly. However, only one of the more than 30 birth experiences detailed by the fathers ended in a less than desirable outcome.

While many of the descriptions of births are quite lovely, and address the exhilaration felt by these fathers, these sections are overlong and present the same or similar emotional reactions over and over.

Since the authors provide no discussion in these last two units, they miss an opportunity to integrate the case study material with the extant literature currently available on the father's role in the birth process. In essence, the fathers have written a book and the authors have written a book and very little effort has been expended to coordinate the two.

A glossary is included as the final section of the book, but is not particularly helpful for several reasons: it uses terms to define themselves (e.g. gestational age is defined as the "exact period of gestation," yet gestation is not defined); terms are inadequately defined (e.g. the Apgar scoring system is included but the terms that correspond to the letters of the name, a = appearance, p = pulse, g = grimace, a = activity, r = respiration, are not included); terms are not cross-referenced; and definitions include other medical terms which are not defined (e.g. silver nitrate is "medication instilled...to prevent ophthalmia neonatorum," but ophthalmia neonatorum is not defined).

While sections of this book may be applicable and helpful to portions of the proposed audience, the text as a whole lacks a sense of interrelatedness and coordination and as such will be of limited usefulness to most individuals seeking a balanced view of the father's participation in labor and delivery.

Mary A. Scoblic, R.N., M.N.
Child Health Nurse Consultant

THE FATHER'S ALMANAC. S. Adams Sullivan. Garden City, NY, Doubleday & Company, 1980 (365 pages; $7.95).

This book is a sensitive, sharing, joyful look at fatherhood written by a father for other fathers. The author presents a composite based on his own readings in and experience with parenting along with the views of 48 other fathers whom he interviewed. Contributors range in profession from roofer to chemist, from banker to bongo drummer and in experience from just starting out to grandfatherhood.

A change of pace from the "how-to" primer on child care, the almanac is written in a light, easy style making it fun to pick up and read straight through or just refer to as an occasional resource. It is designed for an audience of men eager to actively share in raising their children; this book is an excellent choice for expectant or new fathers. It covers the period anticipating the birth of the first child through the preschool years, with a concern that touches everyone involved. The book is written for fathers, but is sensitive to the needs of mothers and children as well. The author's preface admonishes the reader to remember the "child's-eye view". That little person down on the floor who sees the world at an obtuse angle, looking up, is really what this book is all about. Discussion therefore centers on those aspects of fathering which both address the needs of the child and engender satisfaction in the parent.

Parenthood is described as a shared endeavor. Any woman reading this book will be impressed by the sensitivity and understanding shown to the mother as the primary caregiver. Since it is recognized that most men will choose to work outside the home, it is assumed that for the most part it will be the mother who will spend the most time with the children. Consequently, part of the father's role will be in supporting mother through the difficult times. It is biologically impossible for father to share in pregnancy, but by keeping abreast of what is happening within the uterus, father can be a part of the process. What's more, he can help out by assuming some of his wife's daily responsibilities while she goes about the business of nurturing the child within. Father can be supportive if mother experiences a period of emotional let-down following the birth, commonly referred to as the "postpartum blues." Meanwhile, he can be aware of his own brand of "postpartum" depression and allow himself the same freedom to experience it. Sometimes, he goes unrecognized during this period and may actually need permission to feel scared and worried and maybe a little bit jealous. After all, people allow siblings to be jealous of the new arrival, why not fathers? This book gives him the permission.

Since most fathers do not have lots of time to spend with their children, quality of time is stressed. It may be hard to end the working day with innovative, creative child care, but that is what it comes down to for the working father. The author has some wonderful suggestions for accomplishing this, along with a list of resources to which fathers can refer to supplement their skills. Included are "do-it-yourself" tips for building toys and play equipment for toddlers and pre-schoolers. The store bought stock are expensive and shabby. Why not build it yourself, he asks. And while you're at it, he suggests, why not include the children in the building process. These projects are a great way for fathers to be with their children and teach skills at the same time. The author has handy tips on all sorts of joint endeavors with cautions as to what tools are safe in the hands of children at various ages.

This book is geared towards members of intact families. Though there is the admission that many men are divorced and either do not live with their children or are single parents themselves, their problems are not addressed at length. The father who is interested in fully enjoying his children's early years will find a wealth of information and helpful practical suggestions in this volume. Some readers will welcome hints on making bathtime interesting by building bath toys out of household items. Others may find suggested sites for outings useful. Still others may want to know how to find worms for fishing, or what car games seem to keep kids occupied on long trips, or how to design experiments to teach children about electricity. These are some of the inventive sorts of projects to be found in the almanac. When coupled with some basic information about the abilities, needs and care of the infant and young child, the result is both charming and valuable to the new father learning new skills.

Esther Dienstag, MA
Michigan State University

Infant Mental Health Journal, Vol. 2,No. 4, Winter 1981

Journal Reviews

Kunst-Wilson W., Cronewett L: Nursing care for the emerging family: Promoting paternal behavior. *Research in Nursing and Health 4:* 201-211, 1981.

According to the authors, "Margaret Mead is said to have characterized the contemporary view of the father's role in the infant's life as a biological necessity but a social accident" (p. 203). An historical look at the ways in which fathers are included in the parenting process—particularly in their relationship with the infant—would suggest indeed that the father's role is a social accident. Society at large seems to be searching for a way to move from seeing fathers in this way to making socially conscious decisions about how to adequately include fathers in the lives of their infants.

Where do fathers fit in, and how can they be supported, are the questions being asked in this article. The authors are searching for an answer in order to provide guidance to nursing staff as they provide support to fathers antepartum, intrapartum, and postpartum. A set of strategies is defined that nursing staff might use in order to support father's attachment to his infant. But before defining these strategies the authors take us on an historical tour, beginning with the literature that emphasizes the importance of social interaction for the development of the child. They cite literature which has emphasized the importance of the mother in providing the social environment for the child. They also cite more recent literature which clearly raises the question of what the father's role is in the process, and, to a lesser degree, how all family members relate to each other. Accompanying the literature review is an extensive bibliography encompassing both historical and contemporary research.

The authors raise a number of research questions about support systems not only for the inclusion of fathers in parenting of infants, but for the development of the family as a whole. One interesting set of data discussed relates to the way fathers are becoming more increasingly involved during the mother's pregnancy and in the actual delivery of the child—they attend LaMaze classes and are found in the delivery room. What happens, however, is that their involvement decreases when the infant comes home. Some reasons for this are hypothesized, but the most cogent is that there are few social supports for father's later involvement with his infant. There are groups and social norms that encourage father's participation in the preparation for and actual birth of the child; there are no comparable supports for fathers with young infants.

From the scenario presented in the article it is unclear what the father's role should be in the life of his infant, but until that is clear—through research and/or social developments—specific strategies should be developed to support those fathers who are showing an interest in being more actively involved in the life of their infant. If, as Urie Bronfenbrenner states, a child needs the enduring "irrational" involvement of one or more adults in order to develop normally, then where the potential for that irrational involvement exists, it should be supported.

Judith L. Evans, EdD
Director, Family Programs Department
High/Scope Educational Research Foundation

Fein RA: Research on fathering: Social policy and an emergent perspective. *Journal of Social Issues 34:* 122-135, 1978.

Fein argues that the social scientist's study of fathering should be closely linked to contemporaneous events in society and should be viewed within the context of social policy. Perhaps the time has come to gear research efforts to study social events as they are occurring, rather than merely studying the effects of social change after the fact.

In the past 40 years changes have occurred in our perspectives on the father's role in the family. The 1940s and 1950s were dominated by the *traditional* view of father as provider. Father's role was one of economic provider for the family and companion for his wife so that she was "free" to provide nurturance and routine caregiving for their children. This instrumental role for father and nurturant role for mother developed in the context of a society which had few working women and few opportunities for women to gain entrance into the labor force.

During the 1960s a variety of social changes sparked social scientists to become interested in father as caregiver. Over the course of the decade, father's role changed from one of aloofness and disinterest in child development to one emphasizing his role in facilitating successful child development. In this *modern* perspective fathers are seen as responsible for children's sex role identity formation, academic achievement, and moral development, most often defined as the presence or absence of delinquency. However, the model for study of fathering was to investigate the effects of father absence on child development. Few investigators developed programmatic efforts to study actual fathering behaviors as they occurred in father-present homes.

Fein suggests that the traditional and modern perspectives on fathering are being replaced by an *emergent* perspective, which assumes that gestation and lactation are the only parenting behaviors from which fathers are excluded. The emergent perspective is due in part to changes in social policy that have encouraged increasingly large numbers of women to enter the paid labor force. This "flight from the home" by women has a parallel "flight to the home" by men. For example, increasing numbers of men participate in prenatal education classes, attend labor and delivery of their infant, and participate in the routine caregiving tasks associated with parenting. Social science research has discovered that fathers are emotionally invested in the childbirth experience and develop emotional attachments with their infants. Health care hospital practices have changed dramatically during the decade, largely through efforts designed to make the perinatal experience more of a family affair. Still, much needs to be done. Social scientists must increase their study of separated fathers, widowed fathers, divorced fathers, single-parent fathers, stepfathers, and adopting fathers. Through all of this Fein suggests that a key research area of the emergent perspective on fathering is to discover how men are affected by children. Fein implies that social scientists must become actively involved in research activities that are consistent with debates about social policies concerning parenting, and specifically, about fathering. Building closer linkages between social science research and social policy is long overdue in a society that has tended to view social science research and social problems as orthogonal phenomena.

Hiram E. Fitzgerald, PhD
Michigan State University

Index to Volume 2, 1981